RETURN TO JOYFUL LIVING

Reclaiming Life From Fear, Anxiety and Toxic Over-Thinking

To Marjan

With love and blessings,

Lena

LENA GIFFONI

This book describes the author's journey to healing through her experiences along the way. She does not practice medicine, and examples in this book cannot be used as a replacement for the medical advice from a physician or another qualified healthcare provider. The use of this book is not intended as a substitute for personal medical advice. Before making any decision regarding your health or using any remedy described in this book, the reader is advised to consult a healthcare practitioner regarding diagnosis and treatment of his/ her health condition. The author does not take responsibility for any consequences from any treatment, medication or exercise by any person following the examples in this book.

Some names in the book had been changed to protect privacy.
Printed in the United States of America
Cover design: Quest Publications
Cover photo: Kim Giffoni

ISBN: 978-0-9984213-0-8

First of all I dedicate this book to my Creator.

Thank you, Lord, for everything in my life.

To Kim and George.

Your love and support sustained me on this journey.

CONTENTS

Preface vii

PART ONE: Mind Games 1
Chapter 1—What in the World is Going On? 3
Chapter 2—Am I Going Crazy?
       Why Me? and Other Inevitable Questions 9
Chapter 3—Know Thy Triggers 18
Chapter 4—Shame, Guilt and the Stigma of a Mental Disorder..... 33
Chapter 5—Fear and The Gang.. 40
Chapter 6—Mind Games or Breaking the Pattern of Negative Over-
       thinking 48
Chapter 7—Expecting The Tide to Turn 56
Chapter 8—Coping Mechanisms..................................... 66

PART TWO: Body Inside and Out 83
Chapter 9—Nuts and Bolts of Healing............................ 85
Chapter 10—Medications and Natural Remedies 99
Chapter 11—Food and Mood 110

PART THREE: Soul Search...119
Chapter 12—Integrating Theology and Psychology........ 121
Chapter 13—Is It Possible To Justify Suffering? 134
Chapter 14—Dialogues With God.................................. 144
Chapter 15—Lessons in Stillness 155
Chapter 16—Spirit R Us... 162
Chapter 17—Drenched in Light 174
Stress-Relief First-Aid Kit 182
Scripture Verses 183
Acknowledgments... 185
Resources... 187

Preface

*"For I am going to do something in your days
that you would not believe,
even if you were told."*

Habakkuk 1:5

My name is Lena Giffoni and I am a bookaholic. There, I said it. I love books, love the feeling I get by turning pages as well as the thrill of total immersion in the intricacies of plot lines and interactions of characters. I grew up devouring any interesting book I could get my hands on—only it was not easy to find such books. You see, I grew up in the Soviet Union. Shelves of the bookstores were full, and books were published. Unfortunately, most of them were a waste of paper in my opinion; they were mostly boring, authors trying to glorify the achievements of the Soviet people lead by the Communist Party. Some of those books were actually well-written with interesting plots, but they were rather an exception than the norm. Good books were released in small quantities and not wildly available. Some were sold on a black market or distributed through special chain of stores for party elite and for a privileged few.

My paternal grandfather was a high-ranking Soviet army officer. He had access to books and goods many did not. I loved his library, though now I realize it was modest, though to me, who hungered for reading, it was huge. Of course, there was nothing on those shelves that would compromise the beliefs of Soviet people in their government and Communist party. They were supposed to replace God in some way. God, you see, did not exist in the USSR, or so we were taught. So the big portion of Grandpa's library was filled with a full collection of the works of Vladimir Lenin and Karl

Marks, as well as the Great Soviet Encyclopedia. Not surprisingly, I was more interested in reading other books I found there, like stories about adventures of Robinson Crusoe and fights of the Musketeers, struggles of The Count of Monte-Cristo and voyages of Captain Nemo. I read and re-read what was available. I loved it.

When I was about thirteen or fourteen, my father somehow got a copy of Dale Carnegie's *"How to Win Friends and Influence People"*. It was a Russian translation and Dad spent days making five other copies by using an old typewriter and carbon paper. He was supposed to give back all the copies and only keep one. To my understanding, it was a means of paying for the privilege of reading such a rare book. I remember the fifth copy was barely legible, but it was a copy of a book on how one may improve his life nevertheless. No wonder the Soviet government and its censors did not allow books on personal and spiritual development and growth to hit the mass market. If such books were available to the general population, they may actually read them and learn, and question, and want to change their lives!

I once read Emma Larkin's book "Finding George Orwell in Burma," where she describes life in this country. I was shocked to discover that there, good books were even harder to find than it was in my youth. Soviet and Burmese governments did whatever they could to brainwash populations into submission.

One of the ways was to allow people to read only highly censored publications. Because of my upbringing, I am well aware of the power and danger of propaganda. Regimes of any sort want to brainwash their citizens, not truly educate them. I did receive a free education, but in college the most important subjects were History of the Communist Party of Soviet Union, Karl Marx, Friedrich Engels and Vladimir Lenin's Philosophy, Soviet Political Economy and, to top it off, Scientific Atheism!

Back to my love of books. As soon as I gained freedom to read whatever I please, I began collecting books, as many as I could afford, including all different genres. I am well aware that it can become an addiction if I don't keep it under control. Yes, I do have a vast library, but I go through it once in a while to thin it out and give books away. I realize there other ways to read and enjoy books without hoarding them, so I use libraries. When I discovered the Los Angeles library system with its great collection, I became a regular. I usually have a few books and audio books checked out at any given time.

But I still love going to the bookstores to check out what's new and to hold books in my hands. Even if I don't buy them, it still gives me a thrill. More often than not, I bring home a book or two.

A little over ten years ago, I came across the book "The Purpose Driven Life," written by Rick Warren. The title grabbed my attention as well as that of millions of other people, as it turns out. This book became a number one bestseller in non-fiction, second only to the Bible. I bought a copy and had every intention of reading it. When I got home, I put it on a bookcase, hoping to get to it soon…

It was about a year later that I got around to reading it. Designed to be read in forty days, it is a devotional of sorts. A reader is encouraged to take time to think and reflect after each chapter, so I made sure to do just that. As I was reading day after day, I had a strange feeling that I was supposed to write, but how could it be? I had been a high school math teacher for many years. I liked keeping journals since childhood, but writing a book was totally different. It was even more difficult to comprehend, as English is my third language, Russian and Ukrainian being the first two. Regardless of this internal conflict, thoughts about writing persisted for all forty days. Months later I was still longing to write, but what would I write about? Then, a few years later, I got my subject (or rather, it got me), because I was hit by debilitating panic attacks.

At first there were a few journal entries where I poured out my pain and emotions on paper, which proved to be quite therapeutic.

Then I began describing my experience of anxiety to family and close friends. The more open I was about my ordeals, the more people shared their own stories. It was shocking! It dawned on me that there is a silent epidemic of anxiety. As time went by, I was dazed by how many of my friends were suffering just like I was, and they were reluctant to tell their stories. They encouraged me to write this book to help those who suffer. All of us had different causes of anxiety and chose different paths to healing. There are numerous techniques and therapies available that are proven to give positive results. Therapies that helped me the most were not necessarily the best ones for my friends. I felt responsible to find what was right for me. I embraced self-education and found power in seeking answers and gaining knowledge. In my exploration, I realized that regardless of the circumstances in my life, I am created for the joy that only comes from the Ultimate Designer and Creator. *"Weeping may endure for a night, but joy comes in the morning."* (Psalm 30:5, NKJV)

The search for answers on how to achieve this often elusive joy and recovery was indeed an epic journey.

MIND GAMES

CHAPTER ONE

What in the World is Going On?

"And we know that for those who love God
all things work together for good,
for those who are called according to his purpose."
Romans 8:28

I was so sure of the future. It was a year when things were starting to come together for our family: my son was accepted at the same private school that I was teaching math, and my husband's business was finally picking up. We had recently built a new house. Life was beautiful and I felt completely blessed. I loved being a teacher and thought I would be doing it beyond retirement. And then…bam! My life spiraled down, fast.

I remember one day in particular. I had just left the house to go to work when I realized my car had a flat tire. Thankfully the mechanic was passing by and was kind enough to help me with the spare tire. As I was calling in late, I'd become frustrated and stressed. When I got to school, I taught a couple of classes but was feeling off. I experienced tightness in my chest and had heart palpitations. When my left hand began feeling numb, I decided to have my heart checked. I often do things in an unconventional way. I didn't want to go to an emergency room and wait there for hours. Instead, I marched to the nearest cardiologist office during my lunch break. Having no appointment, I told the receptionist that I wanted to be seen. Thankfully, the doctor agreed and after he checked my heart and vital signs, became alarmed and called an ambulance to transport me to the ER. Even though the ER was so close that it shared a parking lot with the cardiologist's office, the doctor was taking no chances of sending me there alone. His office called for an ambulance and within minutes I was attended to by a group of paramedics. They put me on a stretcher and escorted me the whole ten minutes to a building next door. I was scared and thought I might have had a heart attack. The experience was very frightening and surreal. With a history of my father and his father both dying from heart attacks, I was extremely concerned.

A series of tests revealed that I was in no immediate danger. In a few hours I was released to go home. I had to see a cardiologist the following day because of a heart abnormality. After a few hours of additional tests the next day, the doctor told me I had to be admitted to a hospital for an emergency angiogram. I remember bursting into tears as I described to this doctor the events of the past couple of weeks. I became hysterical and was sobbing non-stop, remembering a parent-teacher conference that took place about ten days earlier. It didn't make sense at all. The event seemed rather ordinary. Why did this particular episode affect me so deeply? I've been through difficult situations in my life, some of which seemed much tougher than this. In the past I experienced loss, abuse, betrayal. I was totally bewildered by my extreme reaction. That is when I began recognizing a disconnection between my body's reactions and my thought process, realizing that this situation shouldn't have affected me so dramatically. Why in the world had I begun trembling and hyperventilating uncontrollably whenever I thought of facing a classroom again? I could *not* figure it out. That's the deal with panic attacks. They rarely make much sense. They randomly take over your whole being. I learned that it is the fight-or-flight response of the body to what it perceives as danger.

After the angiogram, I stayed at the hospital for a few days to be monitored. Doctors found a heart abnormality called Mitral Valve

Prolapse. I learned not from doctors but from personal research that people with this heart condition are prone to anxiety and it is more common in women. Later, I also studied the subject of panic disorder.

Within days I realized I couldn't go back to work without feeling anxious and so had to take a leave of absence. Even at home, I had eight to ten panic attacks a day, each lasting over half an hour. Eventually I had to go on disability, as my condition was not improving fast enough. During the first months since being diagnosed, even driving by the school building threw me into a full-blown panic attack. When I had to go back to collect my belongings, I had to hang onto my friend, holding her hand tight. I thought if I didn't do that, I would collapse. I was literally trembling and feeling dizzy.

I had revealing conversations with my doctor and psychologist about why I wasn't able to teach. Part of it was a fear of going into hyperventilation in the middle of a lesson and frightening my students. There were other layers of fears and concerns I discovered in therapy sessions, in conversations with doctors and by studying the subject of anxiety and mental health. My body was responding to various triggers I was not able to recognize at that time. My physical responses didn't make any sense to me.

At first I didn't think a cure was possible. I thought I was going to die; the pain was so intense each time that I was afraid for my life. Knowing that my father died at the age of forty-six from a heart attack may have exacerbated the situation. My poor husband and son bore the greatest burden, seeing me catapulted into a dark emotional and physical place without warning.

A while later, I recalled a few events when I experienced similar symptoms on a much smaller scale. The first time it happened, I was still living in Ukraine. On a particularly hot day, I was huffing and puffing up the hill to get to my place of work and felt tightness in my chest and shortness of breath. I got a bit concerned, but not much. I thought it was just the heat getting to me and didn't go to see a doctor right away. This occurred around the time when things

5

got tense at work: the principal of the school I was working at the time was very unfair with teachers. He acted like a tyrant and it bothered me deeply. The principal was the only male treating all the female staff as if he owned the place. When he brought one of my colleagues to tears over something miniscule, I became upset. I'm always for the underdog and a big desire is for people to get along. Later on I was looking for behavior patterns in my life that led to anxiety. Witnessing unfairness to others is one thing that affects me deeply.

I was back to normal in a few days, tightness in my chest dissipated and I didn't think about this episode until much later.

The second time it happened I had started teaching at a school here in California. The teacher with whom I was sharing a classroom may not have liked me being there. How did I guess? She made a habit of cooking her lunch in our shared classroom in a toaster oven in the middle of my geometry class. I understood she wanted to eat healthy meals and prepare them fresh, but really! I hated confrontation of any sort so I politely asked a few times for her to stop, which she ignored. I had to resolve it somehow, so I complained to my supervisor, to no avail. After a month of these "Geometry Cooking Classes," I dreaded coming to work.

Now that I look back, it doesn't surprise me that eventually I became very stressed. As a result, one not so beautiful morning, I had to be rushed to an ER because I thought I was having a heart attack. The symptoms were similar: shortness of breath, tension in the neck and shoulders, numbness in my left arm down to my fingers, as well as chest pain. Pesky panic attacks mimic heart attacks but thankfully, only in symptoms. In anxiety attacks, the heart is not at risk, even if it feels very much at risk. After a complete checkup, I was released without a diagnosis, and my heart was okay. What a relief! Still, I remember feeling extremely guilty, as nothing was seriously wrong with my health. I alarmed my colleagues and missed a day of work for nothing! Many women feel guilty for bothering others unless they are dying. I will share more about such stoicism and guilt later.

6

Beginning of the Healing Journey

It was nobody's fault. It was the way my body perceived a stressful situation and reacted to seeming threat. This is what happens during anxiety and panic attacks: a natural body response to perceived danger, also called fight or flight reaction. Muscles involuntarily tense up, breathing and heartbeat become rapid and we become basically paralyzed with fear, like a rabbit in front of a rattlesnake.

❝ *It took time to realize that my illness was not going to destroy me*

School administrators and colleagues at my work were concerned. As time passed a few confided in me that they had panic attacks too. I was corresponding via email with the headmaster, with whom I also had a meeting. These conversations contributed to the creation of a school-wide tutoring program that was quite overdue and was launched shortly after. It was the first positive result from a lot of negativity. It helped to look for meaning in life's most unfortunate events and to switch to a positive perspective.

It took time to realize that my illness was not going to destroy me. This challenge in life, like so many others, was to teach and improve me even though in the beginning it was nearly impossible to see any positive aspect of this extremely painful experience. It took a long time but now I can look back with gratitude, appreciating the lessons learned. My hope for all of us is to become better, not bitter as we go through life's inevitable challenges.

At first none of what I was experiencing made any sense at all. I was a total mess, surrounded by almost palpable darkness. Ever so slowly it began to get lighter and lighter. Eventually I saw my situation as a dark tunnel with light shining at the end of it. Finally the day came when a bright light was shining in my life again. My senses returned, I could see, feel, smell and experience joy once again. I was back!

A little over two years—that is how long it took me to overcome severe debilitating panic attacks and get my life back on track. Overcoming mild anxiety relapses took much longer, but those subsided as well. Trust me, it was not easy, but healing proved to be possible. I emerged on the other side stronger, more equipped to face life's inevitable challenges and detours. I became passionate about helping others. Now I look forward to sharing what I have learned along the way with those who seek release from the grip of stress and anxiety.

CHAPTER TWO

Am I Going Crazy? Why Me? and Other Inevitable Questions

"My God, my God, why have you forsaken me?
Why are you so far from saving me,
so far from my cries of anguish?
My God, I cry out by day, but you do not answer,
by night, but I find no rest."
Psalm 22:1-2

Am I Still Normal?

During a severe anxiety attack, a person experiences acutely intense fear of danger. It does not matter if this perception is real or imagined. When we don't know what is going on, it's scary.

I was wondering if I was going crazy and if I would ever be "normal" again. What should be considered normal, anyway? We often look around to see if we "fit in", if our behavior is similar to majority of those around us. Expressing emotions and talking about feelings makes people uncomfortable. Impenetrable emotions and stoic expressions are considered a virtue in many parts of the world. I was raised in such culture. Exposing one's vulnerability was taboo.

People hide what's really going on in their minds for all kinds of reasons. But when we don't open up and talk about feelings, we may think we're the only ones who experience them. I could not imagine even beginning to ask people if they also felt like they were losing their mind. This concealed world of emotions and all these questions made my head spin even more! Losing control of my emotions and what seemed like losing my sanity made me ask the inevitable: what was happening to me, why was I experiencing this turmoil and what was I to do?

Pity-Party or, Why Me?

I was miserable. Most days I wanted to crawl into a hole somewhere and be left alone, at the same time desperately needing compassion and sympathy. I wanted to be free of pain and it was not happening. I wanted a quick fix but I could not find it. As so many of us do when hit with life's adversities, I continually asked, "Why me?" and "Why now?" Soon I realized that dwelling in self-pity led me nowhere.

I began to apprehend that even though I had everything planned, what if my plans were not what God intended? The famous Serenity Prayer says: "God, grant me the serenity to accept the things I cannot change, the courage to change the things I can, and the wisdom to know the difference." Thankfully this "Why me?" period didn't last too long. I came to realize that God does not make mistakes. If something happens in life, there is a definite reason for it. Eventually I began asking different questions: "What can I learn from this experience?", "What is the true Divine purpose for my life?" and "What can I be grateful for?" Words of Apostle Paul resonated with me: *Forgetting the past and looking forward to what lies ahead, I press on to reach the end of the race and receive the heavenly prize for which God, through Christ Jesus, is calling us.* *(Philippians 3:13,14, NLT)* It was encouraging, so there must be a plan from above I am not aware of yet.

Am I Being Punished?
Did I Cause My Suffering?

I think it was inevitable that I faced this question: did my actions cause my suffering? Did I sin so much that God was totally fed up with my inconsistency and disobedience? Were my sins just too heavy and too numerous? How about those times I was breaking my promises to God? Am I doomed for life because of my foolish actions? Again and again I had to remind myself that I am forgiven. I believe that in God's eyes, what is forgiven is forgotten. When I repent of wrongdoing, it is covered with God's unending grace. I can learn from mistakes and move on, without dwelling in the past.

When someone is waving flags of righteousness, saying "You must've done something wrong to deserve such pain," I want to scream at these righteous characters. I don't necessarily want to grab them by the shoulders and shake some sense into them, but I do want to explain so they get it: suffering is not automatically caused by person's sin. There could be so many other reasons unbeknown to us.

❝ *Most days I wanted to crawl into a hole somewhere and be left alone, at the same time desperately needing compassion and sympathy*

Are you familiar with the Biblical story of Job and his compassionate but opinionated friends? Job was a truly blameless man before God, as his Creator admitted Himself, yet he was allowed to suffer. In one day his children and the immense wealth he owned perished. His health also was afflicted. When Job's friends came to comfort him, they took turns trying to convince him that he did something wrong to deserve such punishment. It took God's interference of their conversation to straighten them

11

all out. Creator of It All made a point of reminding these men that He is the only one Omnipotent, He created the Universe and everything in it without help and that He can allow things to happen without needing to explain Himself. Every time I read this story, I get something new from it and highly recommend you read it yourself.

I am not trying to say that I am like Job. Oh no, I am nowhere near his category of super-righteousness. He exemplifies one who, when adversity takes place, allows it to cause growth and maturity. Tending a garden comes to mind as an example. I love to garden and recently planted a few grapevines. In order for them to produce every year, they need to be cut way back. It's not only grapevines; there are so many plants that need to be pruned in order to grow right and produce blooms, fruit or both. If those plants could talk, we would get an earful of cries and complaints.

Just as pain is not a punishment for something I did wrong, a comfortable life is not a reward for all my good deeds. Blessings the Lord bestows upon me are not earned, even though quite often I would like to think they are. These blessings should be treated as such, with thanksgiving and heart-felt gratitude.

Have I Used Up All My Blessings?

I am not alone when on occasion I think in despair: have I used up all my blessings? I will go back and forth, lamenting and dwelling on past mistakes, sins and numerous occasions of disobedience to God. These thoughts show up uninvited to parade themselves before my mind's eyes! In those times I am ashamed and crushed, reliving the guilt of past mistakes. Why do I do that? Human nature, I guess, but enough, already! The past is past and I must let it rest. I learned my lessons (hopefully) and need to move on without the baggage of past issues. I believe God forgives every wrong of the past. Since He does not remind me of any of it, why should I?

I chose to try reassuring faith words: God loves me, He is by my side, I am not alone. The Lord is guiding me towards healing and my divine purpose through these difficult times. He sends me what I call "divine appointments"—meetings and conversations with people that are so timely I can't help but think they are orchestrated by God.

Do I Lack True Faith?

From time to time I was also wondering if I did not believe in my healing strong enough to receive it. A famous passage from the Bible reminded me that if we have faith a size of a mustard seed we could move mountains. In two different Gospels, Jesus talked about this concept of moving mountains with faith.

> "…if you have faith as small as a mustard seed, you can say to this mountain, 'Move from here to there,' and it will move. Nothing will be impossible for you." (Matthew 17:20)

> "Have faith in God," Jesus answered. "Truly I tell you, if anyone says to this mountain, 'Go, throw yourself into the sea,' and does not doubt in their heart but believes that what they say will happen, it will be done for them. Therefore I tell you, whatever you ask for in prayer, believe that you have received it, and it will be yours." (Mark 11:22-24)

Why was this particular teaching of Jesus so important that it was mentioned in two different Gospels? There are a few other verses in the Old Testament where the analogy of faith moving mountains is used. Do we really possess the power to move mountains? Is faith the size of a mustard seed is all that it takes? I don't know for sure how this mountain moving business works, but it must be possible.

> **❝ Reducing stress in my life and slowing down was paramount to getting rid of physical and emotional pain and restore quality of living**

I never actually tried to move the actual mountain nor do I want to test it for a good reason—I revere God and His power. What I do know is that it is crucial to remember the Lord's promises in our day-to-day lives with their challenges and frustrations. There are numerous promises embedded in the Word of God. Different passages may be more relevant to some people than the other. Some, I am sure, are universal.

Thinking about this and other spiritual aspects of healing made me stronger in my faith. I will talk more about it in upcoming chapters.

Is It a Wakeup Call?

The pain of anxiety attacks became a wake-up call. Reducing stress in my life and slowing down was paramount to getting rid of physical and emotional pain and restoring quality of living. My mission then became to learn everything about anxiety triggers. I sought ways to slow down and relax, to manage and release negative emotions and toxic over-thinking. The key was focused motivation to get well. There seemed to be neither free lunches nor magic pills here. Well, there were pills, all right, but no magic behind them…

What Now?

Many people who are facing the challenges of mental conditions go in denial. They are afraid to admit that there is something seriously wrong and that they might need help. In my case, there was no way around it but to face the inevitable. I had to see a doctor, as I was unable to go to work. Getting the right treatment though was an issue, as I did not want to be medicated unless it was absolutely necessary.

Mood disorders need to be diagnosed and properly treated. Unfortunately, in the past, mental illness was greatly feared and was treated with inhumane methods. No wonder that for years the majority of sufferers concealed their illness. Fortunately, times have changed and modern medicine is better equipped to help us face health challenges on different levels, including mental disorders. There are different treatments and therapies available. I had to figure out what specialists I had to find to get the help I needed. There is nothing wrong with seeing a specialist because denying a mental condition does not make it disappear. There is also nothing wrong with seeking the right specialist to meet my specific needs, people with whom I can comfortably discuss all the issues at hand.

Where Shall I Look For Cure?

I desperately wanted to be well and the overachiever in me needed to be proactive, so when I gained energy, I went from psychologist to physician, from chiropractor to acupuncturist, seeking the quickest solution to my problem. I regret not finding a licensed nutritionist and a naturopathic doctor early on.

❝ Many people don't realize there is a possibility of attainable cure for panic attacks and anxiety

In the many conversations with my physician about healing, the doctor agreed that it was not an easy journey. She said that many people don't realize that panic attacks and anxiety can be treated like other conditions regarded as strictly medical. Of course, in the case of treating anxiety, it requires a different path to completely overcome it and there are different ways to approach the treatment. I shunned medication at first as I always prefer the "natural way" to

15

healing. Also, I believed that taking medication was surrendering, and I was unwilling to numb my emotions without exhausting other options first. I was intent on my body healing itself and so began to gather information on holistic treatment.

I am thankful that my family practitioner was supportive of my idea of seeking the natural way to be cured. I was trying to avoid drugs because I remembered watching drug commercials that listed fatigue, nausea and even potential suicidal thoughts as side effects. I wanted to avoid or postpone that kind of treatment at all cost! After struggling for half a year, I finally succumbed to the inevitable: I had to take medication to balance my serotonin level. It was just not happening without it.

I was waiting impatiently for my brain and body to reunite, but not seeing significant long-term results. I wanted to restore my joy, emerge from the cloud of despair to enter the bright side. The struggle wearied me. The chest pain was so severe that many times I felt I would die right then and there from a heart attack, though doctors said my heart was not in danger. When an attack subsided, I welcomed peace and the comfort of inertia, as I was mentally and physically exhausted.

I thought I was losing my sense of self. This overwhelmed and scared person whose mind was spinning out of control was unfamiliar to me. I became cautious of relishing my "illness", maybe even finding significance in my problem…

I had a choice to remain stuck, telling whoever would hear how miserable I was. It made me feel a little better when others expressed compassion and felt sorry for me. Then I remembered my Mom telling me about her classmate in grade school who used to say: "I like to be sick. Everybody is so nice to me and brings me all kinds of treats and pays attention to me. I like it." I examined my soul and concluded that I didn't want to remain paralyzed with emotional immobility, nor welcome pity. That was *not* my identity. I had to find my true self and to deal with circumstances at hand. I decided to do something about it, even if it was just a little bit at a time.

Shrink or No Shrink?

I remember the first psychologist I ever worked with suggested I bring a blanket or a stuffed animal to our sessions. At first I thought I better look for another specialist in the field of psychology as it sounded too silly. Okay, I admit that a couple of times I took my son's stuffed animal with me on flights overseas to keep me company. Also, a commercial comes to mind of a person who goes on a business trip with her child's toy to feel closer to home and family. This whole idea about carrying a soft and squashy security "blankie" and connecting with my inner child sort of made sense, but didn't seem necessary. Because I was committed to trying anything, I did pull something pink and fluffy out of my closet and brought it along to my shrink's office. Later, I didn't see much use in bringing it, maybe just to wipe my tears and nose, so I stopped. Later I found another psychologist who helped me a lot by using a different approach. "Talk therapy" helped to sort things out, regain the feeling of control and lessen the anxiety-related symptoms.

All these unanswered questions lingered in my head. Obsessing certainly didn't help with answers and solutions. Slowly, one by one, answers began to emerge.

I was determined to find out what makes me anxious and what can I do about it. At the beginning stages, the last question sounded more like: "is there *anything* I can do to feel better?" With research, trial and error, I discovered many tips that helped me along the way and many of which I still use. At first I was impatient with trying only one method and waiting for weeks to see if it was working. As soon as I read or heard something that gave hope, I put it to immediate use.

17

CHAPTER THREE

Know Thy Triggers

"And I tell you, ask, and it will be given to you;
seek, and you will find;
knock, and it will be opened to you."
Luke 11:9, ESV

Predisposition and Triggers

Sometimes anxiety is caused by something tangible, like a loss or tragedy, which is justifiable, given extreme emotions under difficult circumstances. But what if anxiety shows up suddenly, from nowhere, sprouting from a benign situation? I've been in unnerving situations and faced tragedy, but what sent me into a disabling tailspin was not even close to that!

A person may feel panicky in an extremely stressful situation. His heart will race and he'll have shortness of breath, queasy stomach or sweaty hands. Usually these symptoms go away shortly after the event that caused anxiety has passed. Sometimes people worry for days or weeks before a major decision is to be made and nervousness will go away once the problem is resolved. There are levels of anxiety. There is stress that can be easily controlled or which is fleeting, and then there is severe anxiety that may require medical attention. How does one recognize when to seek help? When does the "normal" become "abnormal"? Seeing a primary care physician and verbalizing all concerns is a good first step.

Anxiety-Provoking Thoughts and Situations

Awareness of what triggers anxiety and fears is necessary. Usually we have patterns—situations that certainly will cause stress and anxiety. Often they are rooted in childhood experiences. It is easier to discover these patterns by talking to a therapist. Then they can be pinpointed and worked with.

Anticipating challenges or disasters is a healthy thing, and can be preventative. Dwelling in negativity brings the opposite and may be damaging. An expression "a coward dies a thousand deaths" comes to mind. Strangely, if I think too much about diet and health, I have a higher chance of being sick, and I have sometimes developed pain and symptoms. Have you ever heard of sympathy pain, i.e., someone tells you about pain they are experiencing and all of a sudden you have the same pain? Such pains lingered for a long time and finally went away after comprehensive tests. If I listen to a health program or watch TV shows about new diseases, I might develop a fear of such diseases. At times I wonder: is it possible to calculate potential risk without over-thinking?

Overwhelmed

I realized I don't have to be perfect, something I struggled with throughout my life. I had to learn to let things go and to delegate so I can be less anxious. It also gave me time to focus on God. A story of sisters Mary and Martha from the Gospel of Luke comes to mind. One was completely overwhelmed with preparations to be done for a feast. Believe me, I can relate! I love having company, but preparations used to turn me into a nervous wreck! Everything had to be perfect and my pride would not allow help from my guests. If I only had a sister handy to share the responsibilities! Well, in the case of Mary and Martha, one was cooking and cleaning in a frenzy, while the other was listening at the feet of Jesus. Which was the right way? Of course, listening to our Lord, you would say. Right, but what if it was you and guests are already there (Jesus for one) and to prepare a decent dinner you would have to fetch the water, take care of the burning woodstove, clean without a vacuum or cleaning products. Oh, did I mention there was no electricity and refrigeration, so all food had to be prepared fresh? You get the picture. It is important to show hospitality and feed your family, no doubt, but I need to get my priorities straight. Time and time again I got so busy in life that I forgot to focus on the Lord first. I needed to get my priorities reorganized.

Believe me, it was easier said than done. Thankfully, at the time of this whole ordeal with severe panic attacks, I was fortunate to have the luxury to drastically reduce my responsibilities. I can't believe that I am being thankful now for being practically immobile, in pain and on disability for my condition! Nevertheless, because of it I focused on spending time in solitude, seeking God.

I often wondered what I would have done differently in the past, when I felt responsible of taking care of everyone in my family: a small child who had to be chauffeured to and from school and activities; a husband who struggled to build a business which took almost all of his time and energy; a very sick mother in-law who required medical attention and care as well as meeting the needs of an extended family. Yes, I also had a full-time job and did all my cooking, cleaning, shopping and coupon-clipping. There were days when I would drive to work (thankfully, my son was at the same school at which I taught at the time), teach, take my son, go home, pick up my mother-in-law with her wheelchair and oxygen tank, drive her to see a doctor or to the hospital, stop at the grocery store on the way back and cook dinner afterwards. How did I do it? I have no idea—I just did. There are so many women out there who are overwhelmed, overworked and exhausted. Yet they don't know how to ask for help or delegate. There is also a possibility of confrontation with family members. Who wants to hear kids whining when they are asked to do chores? There is also the whole issue of doing things just right. For a perfectionist, it is easier to do everything myself than to have dishwasher loaded in a wrong way or see dishes put away in the wrong places. Convincing myself it was okay not to have my laundry done in a particular way was not easy. Nevertheless I had to let go and ask for help. I realized things didn't have to be done perfectly as long as they were done. I gained a simplified life from this survival mode. I was just not able to do much, so I had to ask for and receive help.

I used to run numerous errands to a point of exhaustion. With a new mindset, I realized I didn't have to do everything at once. At first, in my fight against stress and anxiety, I decided to follow a rule of three errands at a time. Now I can enjoy doing numerous things in a day and feel fulfilled and powerful. On the rare occasion when I have one of "those" weeks, when the to-do list gets long and it begins to overwhelm me, I switch back to a short list of three, maybe four errands, and stick to it. It definitely happens around the holidays when we have so many things on our minds. That is when many of us may benefit from paying extra attention to prioritizing, using discipline and do less.

I also make sure that I keep the Sabbath as the Lord's—a day when I don't work. Easier said than done, right? Finally, with enough practice, it became automatic. I don't garden, clean, do dishes or laundry. I rest, read, spend time with my family and friends. When I was working full-time, I was so overwhelmed with work and managing a household that I was not giving my full attention to God. I attended church, I prayed in the car while driving, but it was not the relationship with my Creator that I so needed and longed for. I thought I didn't have time, but the truth was, I had my priorities seriously mixed up. That had to change.

Here's another thing: when I get stressed and overwhelmed by the endless list of errands in my head, I can give it all to the Lord and feel the tension dissolve. I keep praying, admitting that the Lord is in control of my life: "Father, I don't have to be in control, you are. I don't have to do it all. Please take care of me and all my needs. Thank you for the peace of mind and serenity you are giving me. I am relaxed in your hands and you are restoring me, my body and my soul. Amen."

Responsibilities of a Caregiver

Many women are conditioned to care for others to the point of self-sacrifice. It is especially true if a girl is the oldest child in the family and becomes responsible for her siblings and the majority of chores. I was no exception. My mom often worked long hours and two jobs with long commutes, so I was expected to have numerous responsibilities around the house and do well in school from a young age. I did what was expected of me but being burned out was a natural state. As I got older it became more difficult to carry a heavy load of responsibilities. I put enormous pressure on myself to be a Cinderella, answering any demand and request that came my way, not knowing it was possible to ask God for guidance to navigate and prioritize. If I had been aware of such inaudible conversations with my Creator, I would have been more equipped to prioritize. Doing everything and helping everyone, playing Superwoman, may make me feel needed but was I supposed to do it all the time? Taking care of myself, my physical and spiritual well-being allows me to help others. On the other hand, when I am burned out, I feel useless, which triggers resentment, anger, loneliness and guilt for not doing it all with a smile on my face. Though serving is a great gift, becoming overwhelmed by constant overload is a reality for many. Women especially are programmed to take care of others first, but as in the case of an emergency on an airplane—we must put that oxygen mask on first, then we will be able to help others!

The Downside of Stoicism and Resilience

Many situations taught me to be strong. I always sought the silver lining and thought I had to be strong, not showing my true emotions. I took pride in my resilience because I was praised for it early on, which helped me to quickly recover from hurtful situations without showing emotion. There were many things I told no one about. I stuffed whatever emotions I felt deep inside and moved on, telling myself and others that I was fine. As a child,

I was given to crying and was teased for it, thus I tried to swing over to extreme stoicism and to not show weakness. I did not realize then that showing weakness and vulnerability was actually a sign of strength and courage. I did not allow myself to stop and reflect how I felt even over loss of family members. I was afraid to allow myself to deeply feel emotions, especially negative ones.

This veneer of stoicism that accumulated over the years wore off under emotional strain and I dearly paid for suppressed feelings I hid in the pressure cooker of the soul, and when they did burst, manifested as severe panic attacks. The result was quite unappealing and messy, as you would expect from a pressure cooker explosion.

Resilience vs. Vulnerability

Through various experiences in my life, I've learned that I'm resilient; actually, I'm quite tough. But I'm vulnerable, too—what a dichotomy! How can I be both? And can't vulnerability be a gift and a blessing?

I was brought up burdened with responsibility tinged with guilt. I was expected to accomplish much to be acknowledged and praised. So I became an achiever—not exactly an overachiever—but I would push myself enough to be recognized.

Conflict Avoidance

Instances of emotional and physical abuse in my youth resulted in a deep fear of confrontation. I learned to recognize potential conflicts and avoided them at all cost. Being hit hard by men on a few occasions for speaking my mind only reinforced it.

My past avoidance of any and all confrontation eventually backfired. I had to change, but how? When I adopted my little dog, I realized how protective I was of her. But in the past, there were times I would not go for a beach walk for fear of loose dogs. My yappy little doggy changed that in a matter of days. As it turned out, she loved running on the beach and she would bark and try to intimidate any dog that would come near her, except when a dog was ten times her size, brave girl that she is…she would run and hide behind me. And I would become protective instantly, forgetting about my past fears and face the big dog, yelling "no!" After a few times, I was completely cured of my fear of big dogs. Isn't it fascinating? I realized I could change my mindset and be fearless.

Women are often predisposed to please even without being abused. We pile things up on our to-do lists. First, we do it to be liked and second, to avoid ruffling feathers and creating conflicts. For years to come, any possibility of potential confrontation caused discomfort, later causing stress and anxiety. Thus, confrontation or even a possibility of confrontation became one of my definite anxiety triggers. I began wondering if it was possible to prepare myself for confrontation without trying to avoid it at all cost. I needed to face my fears one at a time. It helped me to imagine the verbal exchange, as such conversations are never easy. When someone I face is offensive or argumentative, I need to ask God to give me power to respond with wisdom or to retreat in peace.

I am learning to discern when criticism directed at me is constructive and when it is destructive and therefore reflecting only the internal conflicts of the other person. I ask myself, what are the motives of those who criticize me? Shall I respond at all and if yes, then how? There are numerous books written on the subject of conflict resolution and they were a great help in eradicating a sense of inferiority and in building "emotional muscle". Timidity was slowly replaced with self-confidence. Though I was taught that good girls should always be nice and I like being loving and kind, when someone treats me unfairly, I need strength and courage to speak for myself or on behalf of those being mistreated.

Destructive Thoughts

As I was driving home from work on Kanan Road one night in the pouring rain, rocks were falling from cliffs onto the road. I was not going fast, but when I saw a boulder in the middle of my lane, traffic coming from the opposite direction and cars behind me, I swerved to the right, but unable to avoid it. The left wheel and the rim were damaged. I felt lucky that I that I had cell phone reception in that part of the canyon and could call. I had just picked up dinner for the family, so I was able to eat and not starve during those two hours that I had to wait for road service to come. It was a busy night in the canyons as falling rocks had damaged many cars.

This episode could have become an anxiety trigger. I've read about people whose panic attacks were caused by car accidents. Thankfully I was not one of them. I did not get fearful of driving even though I did start praying more during my commute. On foggy and rainy days, when it was hard to see not only the cliffs and mountains surrounding this winding mountain road but the road itself, I would imagine being home already, enjoying dinner with my guys. Such anticipation and projection into a pleasant near future took my mind off being fearful.

Driving on the same road and seeing the beauty of surrounding nature bathed in brilliant California sunshine is breathtaking. Unfortunately, in times of internal battles with anxiety, beautiful surroundings were lost on me. Once, I even had a fleeting thought of ending my life. As I was driving along the winding canyon road high in the mountains, unsettling thought snuck into my mind: would my husband and son be better off without me? Just a twirl of the wheel and they will be free from witnessing my pain… but instantly I was reminded that it couldn't be the answer to ending suffering: theirs and mine. I also remembered that this was my favorite prayer drive. Though that suicidal thought never resurfaced, I feel compelled to mention this episode. I read stories about mental illness and the possible side effects of medications used to treat such conditions. They suggest how common suicidal thoughts are among sufferers. In many cases, it was a connection to God and the power of prayer that helped to restore the will to carry on and find new purpose in life.

Facing Mortality

When I was struck with a severe anxiety attack accompanied with physical pain, I felt I was dying. It was terrifying! After doctors ran numerous tests and I was properly diagnosed, I had to believe that anxiety, as lethal as it felt, was not going to kill me. I also had to accept that death is inevitable, even if not imminent. Relinquishing the false sense of control of that, I *can* try to prolong my life by embracing health, but I'm not immortal. What I *can* control is how I live my life, what I believe and the impact I make on those around me.

Brutal anxiety attacks were not my only health concern in recent years. When an MRI report showed a tumor in my ankle, I was in shock. It was damaging the bone and a bone graft surgery was done, with almost two months of wheelchair convalescence. When I first learned about a tumor, I was devastated. Was it benign? Would I be able to resume my regular activities after rehabilitation? Again, I asked that silly rhetorical question: "Why did this happen?" I try to come up with an answer, as it helps to see some meaning behind life's seemingly random events. But the Lord used me as an example to others, of relying on Him in every situation. This event became an encouragement to others because I was open about what I underwent.

The long recovery from this complicated surgery reminded me of a time I was bedridden with anxiety, knowing that this was one of the best ways God could grab my attention. If something were to happen to my leg or foot, I would still come to work, even if in a wheelchair. I loved my job and was totally dedicated to what I was doing. Ironically, after surgery, I was doing just that: going to work in a wheelchair. The Lord has very interesting ways to confirm His purposes.

A while ago, my husband's business associate was diagnosed with last stage pancreatic cancer. For over a year, her condition remained undiagnosed and when she finally found out, she received a very grim prognosis—only weeks to live. Unfortunately, this prediction proved to be true. Why did it have to happen? Why didn't the Lord cure her on the spot? Could He? There is no doubt in my mind of His omnipotence. Yes, He is able to heal, so why doesn't He do it every time? One thing we need to remember...He has His purpose for everything; He created the universe (including us) and has a plan for everything and everybody. We don't know when our time will run out, but we are destined to depart and be with our heavenly Father one day. In our culture, we don't dwell on the inevitability of death. We collectively pretend that we are going to live forever and the media propagates body image and entertainment as the most important things in the world. We need to make peace with our own mortality and its inevitability. We have to accept that the Lord does not cure terminally ill patients all the time, as unfair as it seems. It is especially difficult to witness someone die young. The best thing for us to do is pray.

When desperate situations arise, we relentlessly ask "Why me, Lord, why, why me?" At times, I inevitably asked the same question: Why did I have to go through all of this pain? There are possible answers, but the main idea is that everything is a learning experience, and often we learn best through painful ones. There must be a reason for the expression "growing pains," which not only relates to physical pains of growing teenagers. Yes, we learn best through trials and, unfortunately, through pain.

Anxiety Strikes at any Age

I remember feeling extremely anxious before tests when I was in school. I wondered how my students felt when I taught them a difficult concept in geometry class. When my son tried to teach me to play a videogame, I was at total loss. I couldn't move the character where I wanted it to go. I was frustrated and even felt panic creeping in.

I believe I was predisposed to anxiety and nervousness since childhood. I was a nervous wreck before tests in high school and college, before job interviews or major airplane trips. My stomach would churn and I would feel my heart pounding. At the time I didn't think anything was seriously wrong with me—I thought that was how my body reacted to stress, so I dismissed it.

Between pressures and demands of academic excellence and sports, many children feel overwhelmed. Teenagers who battle anxiety are even less equipped to deal with it than those who are older. If adults get frightened, discouraged and overwhelmed, I can only imagine what children go through. I don't want to be a teenager again, with all the pressure and demands, especially when I recall my mom pushing me to be my very best and I felt I was failing her. Kids try to shake off anxiety, but if those attempts fail, they try self-medication with drugs and alcohol. In our culture, these "remedies" are all too accessible. People of all ages and especially children need to learn techniques to reduce stress in their lives. We must advocate for programs in school that deal with this issue of modern day living. Taking prayer out of everyday life seems like a big mistake to me. I grew up in an atheistic society and I wish I had been taught how to build up my relationship with my Creator through prayer and stillness when I was little.

Perils of Perfection

At times I read books or watched TV to escape, and then felt guilty for not being productive. I felt guilty for experiencing pure pleasure of escaping and not contributing, for not doing something meaningful and productive, for not being perfect! We set ourselves up for definite failure if we expect to be perfect all the time. We can conduct many things to perfection, often at the cost of being overwhelmed and stressed beyond belief.

Confessions of a Reformed Perfectionist

For a long time I struggled to have good grades in school. I was the youngest in my class and felt pressure to succeed, not realizing I was competing against students a year older. I was determined and

28

so became a straight "A" student in my senior year. In college the story repeated itself—I was the youngest, desperately trying to fit in socially and to succeed academically. I was studying mathematics and it was very challenging.

Somehow, having all in order helps me to feel in control. In my healing, I learned to let go of unconscious obsessions. My mom used to tell me not to "distort" my attention. There is no such expression in English, but she meant that I was to focus. Recently I learned it's okay to "distort" and have a few unfinished projects lying around the house. I have begun five different journals unintentionally because I liked getting a pretty new journal and begin writing in it. Time would pass and I would get another pretty journal. I don't feel frustrated now that I have six or so different ones: a gratitude journal, church sermons journal, a journal of letters to my son, etc. Then there are a couple of them wherein I wrote for a while and then started another one without using up all the pages in the first one. (Gasp! How could I? It's a sin!) I made peace with it. I don't need to over-think silly journal entries.

We often "contract" perfectionism from family members, close friends or teachers when growing up. Many little girls are taught to do things just right: "Never start something you are not going to finish" and "If you are not going to go it right, don't do it at all"

I like "Perfect is the enemy of good" and "There is a plan, and then there's what happens"—these sayings are more useful in everyday life. Perfectionism is a roadblock on a way to life filled with joy and happiness.

There is nothing wrong with striving to do things precisely and very well when it is important, unless it becomes obsessive. I had to retrain myself to let certain things go and not judge myself so hard. Now having achieved balance, I can thrive again in bursts of high-speed living, the pace I love and craved for years. Then I have to pause, reflect and smell the roses, sometimes literally. I want to learn to be content and fulfilled in things big and small.

As silly as it sounds I used to stress about unfinished knitting projects. How terrible is it to not finish one scarf but start a new one, right? Just because I like that pretty yarn doesn't mean I shouldn't do what I want! I eventually made peace with the imperfect house, unfinished journals and incomplete projects. What a relief!

I once visited a church in Culver City, where I met a lady about my age, Janet. The conversation angled toward my condition. She had asked if I worked and my answer included the usual: I am on disability because of panic attacks. Allowing myself to be vulnerable freed me and also allowed me to relate to and help others not to feel so alone in their pain. Right away Janet opened up about her own experience with anxiety. She came from Georgia a while back with her husband and little daughter who was about one and a half at the time. Janet's mother, with whom she was very close, passed away a year before. This southern belle was as sweet as they come. She was taught since childhood to keep appearances and be strong, and she did just that. But without extended family and friends in her new city, she felt lonely and even desperate at times. We then spoke about perfectionism. She admitted that it was predominant throughout her life. We compared our anxiety experiences and she was glad to find someone who could relate, as for months she was suffering in silence, thinking she was losing her mind.

The most common and painful confession of those who shared with me their emotional journeys through anxiety was their suffering in silence. I wonder how many people are trying to toughen up through anxiety, concealing in fear the torment that haunts them. They feel near death with the loss of reason yet don't want to admit something is not well with them. Panic disorder affects many "overachievers." I was infected with perfectionism at an early age. It may propel achievement, but it can have a side effect of toxic emotions, as I experienced. Now I am the first to admit I do need help, that I am not flawless. I can't be perfect.

Being Hard on Myself

The common problem for conscientious overachievers is not recognizing their accomplishments, but rather focusing on what else needs to be done. Being dissatisfied leaves no room for being grateful for all the gifts and blessings bestowed upon us. I need to acknowledge what good things I have done. When I was beating myself down, I turned to writing lists of blessings and achievements, which helped significantly.

In Life Coaching practice, there is a form I ask my clients to fill out before each session. It is set to remind a person what has been accomplished in the past month so she can recognize her progress, even if minimal in her mind. People who hire a life coach are often "overachievers in a rut" or "in disguise," who don't like their present life or lack of forward movement. I am one of these people, so I realize how important it is to give yourself credit, giving due glory to God who gifted you with talents and skills and to celebrate what He enabled you to do.

I think I finally learned to be emotionally lighter. When I was younger I took everything in life too seriously. Lightening up alleviates a lot of stress and opens a path to unobstructed joy!

Shame vs. Guilt

I see shame and guilt as totally wasted emotions. Yet most of us waste hours, days, weeks or even years totally entangled in them. Some say we clothe ourselves with guilt, shame and fear. These emotions are as dirty rags we put on top of royal robes. The beautiful clothing is underneath it all, but we decide to pull the filthy ugly garments over our heads again and again, not realizing that we must remove them once and for all to reveal the royal dress hidden underneath.

When I was ashamed, it stirred me deep in my soul, regardless if I did something I was not proud of or a condition I was in. It could be provoked by questions like: how in the world did I do that?! Or it could be something that happened to me I did not want others to see for fear of making me less of a person I strive to be. At times I was surrounded by people who were not helping to shake the guilt off but who piled back up a triple portion of it. I wanted to cover my shame by all means. I think when people lie or drink alcohol in excess, they may be attempting to cover the shame hidden deep inside. I am ultimately ashamed of betraying God by not becoming my very best. It is complicated. Admitting sin, repenting and asking for forgiveness was my way of dealing with guilt before God.

CHAPTER FOUR

Shame, Guilt and the Stigma of a Mental Disorder

"Do not be afraid; you will not be put to shame.
Do not fear disgrace; you will not be humiliated."
Isaiah 54:4

Only a short while ago, an HIV positive diagnosis was not only frightful but also shameful. Upon discovery, this disease was not widely researched and therefore terrifying. People who suffered from AIDS became outcasts.

Progress in treatment as well as attitude and awareness is evident. Historically, mental and mood disorders were widely misunderstood and treated harshly and barbarically. We must look at certain mental diseases in a similar way. Many sufferers forsake treatment out of fear of societal repercussion or due to lack of understanding of its benefits. Many still suffer in silence, ashamed and afraid of ridicule. Traditionally, mental illness was perceived as something reprehensible. It was not often discussed or understood. Unfortunately, studies show that conditions may worsen if not timely diagnosed and addressed properly.

Recently, new light has been shed and awareness has been raised on mental disorders and as a result, more people can attain wellbeing and happiness instead of wandering in the dark.

Thankfully, sufferers can be more informed with research findings and available treatment.

In biblical times, any kind of physical deformity was viewed as a curse. There was an occasion, described in the Gospel of Mark, where disciples asked Jesus if blindness was a fault of a man or his parents. There was not even a question if blindness was not a punishment of some sort. Restored sight is the most mentioned healing miracle in the Bible. Today we wear glasses or contact lenses without wondering if we sinned to incur such infirmity. Cure for many vision impairments is common and we don't think twice before going to an optometrist. The attitude towards mental illness is still quite different.

Loneliness and Withdrawal

When I realized I was having panic attacks, I was ashamed to admit it to people, even close friends. I felt as if I was losing my mind and feared being perceived as a crazy person; thus, I became a slave to fear. I was experiencing severe physical pain caused by anxiety, and was feeling isolated. Usually outgoing and friendly, I didn't feel like seeing anyone for long periods of time. The thought of being in public, having to interact with others, was unbearable. I could not bring myself to share my experiences with friends who might say yet again: "Snap out of it!" or to see a blank stare from a person who was not able to relate and understand what I was going through. I desperately needed compassion, but not many were equipped to offer help.

Friends and Community

Many of us don't trust others in sharing our inner world, knowing we all have flaws of character that show up in mean and hurtful ways. Even old friendships fall apart from a few harsh words spoken in argument.

We can be judged and misunderstood at times, but it doesn't justify living in fear of rejection and betrayal. Numerous studies show emotional and health benefits of being in a community. We are created as social beings who need human affection and interdependence as a human race. In our culture, the deep bond with others has been supplanted with technology and media. Many studies prove that people with deep ties to their communities are healthier, happier and even live longer! These communities can be where people grew up, their families or a network of close friends.

Though it may be challenging to open up and speak candidly, leaving aside fear of betrayal or ridicule, we are rewarded with comfort. Having even one confidant is a true blessing. How can we know whom to trust? There is an interesting phenomenon of people sharing their life stories with total strangers on a plane, train, or bus. The rationale is that we may never see those people again. Practice of confession in Catholicism is somewhat similar in the same sense, as a person who confesses remains incognito. For people who don't confide in travel companions or priests but not ready to share with people around them, talking to a psychologist may be the option.

When I was hit by bouts of anxiety on a regular basis, just saying hello to a neighbor was a challenge. How could I explain my feelings to someone who never experienced what I was going through? When I began feeling better for days, weeks, and later months, I would return to my cheerful, social self. Then out of the blue—anxiety recurred without obvious trigger. It made me avoid conversations and withdraw for long periods of time. Because I'm more of an extrovert, this ordeal changed my personality, which I loathed. Contrary to my usual, fun-loving nature, I was avoiding parties, neighborhood gatherings and church events. I usually went to church every Sunday, but in this season of my life, I missed many services, as I could not force myself to face people. What I was experiencing was a form of agoraphobia and as with other irrational fears, my reasoning did not make much sense. I expected people to be judgmental, ignorant or critical and I was too vulnerable to face that, so my natural instinct was to hide.

I am blessed to have friends from different cultures, religious affiliations and backgrounds. Their support was invaluable, but there was something extra special in knowing that people were praying for me. Some prayed with me in person, others over the phone and many others prayed what is called an intercessory prayer (petitioning God on my behalf). I am forever grateful to the Lord and them. I know numerous people prayed for me at the school at which I taught and at my home church, even as I isolated myself.

I brought church home by watching "televangelists," and the trial I was enduring emotionally and physically resulted in my spiritual revival. I was praying more, reading spiritual literature and discovered God-inspired messages on TV and the Internet. It was so comforting to listen to people who suffered through their own trial and emerged stronger, praising God for his Divine guidance and comfort along the way. I needed to share with someone who could identify with my experiences but didn't know where to look. I began seeking forerunners who came out on the other side, healed. Unfortunately, finding such people proved to be a great challenge.

Expressing Pain and Emotions

At first I was ashamed to share my condition. I felt I was losing my mind. Little did I know there are many people who felt as I did and experienced symptoms similar to mine. Yet we had no idea how real a cure could be.

Many suffer in silence, spiraling down into despair and depression. It may be especially difficult for men to open up as they don't want their strength to be questioned.

Some try to hide their true feelings even from family members and close friends in fear of being labeled "emotionally unstable" or "mental." They don't want to be perceived as "crazy people." Others go into denial or remain afraid and lonely, not knowing help is available. Unfortunately, spouses and friends of sufferers usually don't know what their loved ones are dealing with. It's not that you can just "snap out of it," though you wish you could.

It took some time, but finally I was able to open up about my anxiety. In hindsight, I should've created or joined a support group. It is so much easier now, knowing what I know, realizing how many people are suffering as I did. But in the beginning I was frightened, misunderstood and alone in misery.

Illusion of control

In case of mental illness, all the illusions of being in control of situations vanish and we are left to deal with raw emotions that we seem to have no power over.

Many people don't want to see a doctor for any condition, mental or physical, because they are afraid to give up the illusion of control. Here is an interesting question: what can we control and what can we not? The Serenity Prayer comes to mind. The things we can control in life and the things we can change are very similar. With enough repetition we can change and control our reaction to events in our lives, finding meaning and positive outcome.

Losing Control

For me, one of the worst things about going through bouts of anxiety, depression or anger was losing control: of my mind, my body and my life. I was in physical pain, yes, but not being able to keep in check what was going on in my head—that was disturbing! It took me years to graduate from being a depressed teen to a woman who learned to appear to have it all together. After all, we can't control what happens to us, but we can control what happens *in* us, right? But for the longest time, I could not figure it out nor did I see a way out of this predicament. I was angry that I could not just will myself out of this downward whirlpool of emotions. I had a habit of trying to orchestrate every detail of my life and became an over-thinker extraordinaire. I was a perfectionist, after all. Even though deep inside I always knew this sense of control was only an illusion and the only one who was in control at all times was God, almighty and powerful Creator of it all.

Opening Up and Sharing

Have you ever dreamt you were walking down the street, naked? I haven't myself, but I've heard it's common. Sharing my experience of panic attacks was a baring of my soul, leaving it vulnerable to judgment, like disrobing in public. I had to do it, pushing through fear, if I wanted to find others who could relate to my pain. Unfortunately, I encountered many more people who were still suffering than those who already won the battle with anxiety. It then became my personal mission to learn from books and other sources how to overcome anxiety and be equipped to help others. At first I was ashamed to share, then I realized this is how God equipped me to overcome obstacles, and is the very thing that may comfort and help others undergo similar circumstances. It changed my perspective from desperate "Why me?" to hopeful "Teach me, Lord, and guide me!"

As a result of my openness on this subject, I had many people confiding in me about their anxiety or depression, feeling safe after my sharing. They hid this pain for so long, embarrassed, scared and confused, not realizing they weren't alone in the need to share their fears with someone who may understand and relate.

When I would speak to a small group of people, I began to recognize the glee of recognition in some faces. After I would tell my story publicly a few people usually came forward and confided in me privately. Sharing my vulnerabilities made it safe for them to open up. Their pain, shame, guilt and life suffering was all too familiar. Sometimes family members of sufferers would consult me, as they were confused by the behavior of their loved ones. They helplessly witnessed the torment, but had no point of reference. It reminded me how my loved ones tried to advise me to "snap out of it". Oh, were these dear ones ever clueless.

After many encounters with fellow sufferers, I knew that there was a silent anxiety epidemic out there, and that it had to be addressed, but what could I do? I shared what I learned and mentioned numerous books I read on the subject. But I saw that people were relating to my story more than they could to books written by professionals in a mental health field.

Everybody has a story, but not everyone has an opportunity or calling to share his or her story with the world. Paralyzing fear and shame sometimes prevents us from reaching out to encourage a person who can gain from our experience. We may not realize the important role we are given because of the blinding burden we carry, and yet there's redemption in our helping and lovingly supporting others. Having this purpose in my suffering took me from self-centeredness to a sense of charity and mission. But I didn't arrive at this attitude before going through a grieving process. I had to experience the pain and sorrow to emerge, ready to help others. I was then willing to openly share very personal experiences and realized many of those I spoke to were starved for understanding and confidence.

I began to wonder if my extreme pain and subsequent freedom was preordained. I had zeal to write about my journey to recovery. I simply had to share my story, to give someone hope of recovery. My story may bring better understanding of Panic Disorder and inspire proactivity.

CHAPTER FIVE

Fear and The Gang

"For God gave us a spirit not of fear but
of power and love and self-control."
2 Timothy 1:7

Anxiety, fear, depression and anger—these emotions seem to be different, yet all of them seem to stem from the same place of uneasiness deep inside. These emotions are powerful and can become debilitating. When we first try to shake off the unpleasant or disturbing feelings but without success, don't we have a tendency to clam up, scared? I've been there, thinking I was losing my mind and afraid I will never be "normal" again. I was unable to control it, which made it even more frightening. I tried and tried to shake it off, but to no avail. Our bodies react to stress in various amazing ways and it's totally fascinating!

In my case, depression and anxiety were sort of playing a tug of war and anxiety usually won. Depression was lurking close by, ready to devour what was left of me after anxiety temporarily loosened its grip. I needed a break from these excruciating moods. I resolved to take action, even if it was the last thing my body wanted to do. I would put a grin on my face, resembling that of an orangutan taking a "selfie". But somehow the grin was working. A study at one of the universities revealed that clinically depressed patients who were required to stand in front of a mirror and grin from ear to ear felt significant improvement as compared to the other group of patients who were treated in the conventional way with medication. No wonder there is a saying "laughter is the best medicine."

Depression

To dread getting out of bed on a rainy morning is one thing, but when it lasts for days, without the energy to move, is another story altogether. It's a mystery that an overall healthy body can react this way. The motions of morning rituals took huge effort. Sometimes I'd be still wearing a robe, pajamas and slippers when taking my child to school, hoping not to be pulled over...

When the last thing on my mind was to do something, that is exactly when something had to be done! I had to resolve to roll out of bed regardless how low I felt. This perpetual numbness had to end somehow, preferably sooner. It required action. I resolved to take action even if it was the opposite of what my body wanted to do. I forced myself to roll out of bed, literally dragging myself out, putting on walking clothes and leaving with a cup of coffee.

I know how to look at things negatively, which leads to being anxious and depressed. It took a lot of practice to become an expert at being depressed and anxious. What do I mean by that? I recall very well my body and facial expressions when depressed or anxious. It took time to unlearn being depressed and to learn how to be joyous. By just changing my body and facial expression, I was halfway there. Have I achieved being the happiest person in the world every day of my life? Of course not, but I learned how to bounce back and be optimistic in many situations. I learned how to be proactive instead of reactive, not becoming a victim of circumstance but being in control of my emotions.

As with other mental conditions, triggers for depression can be biochemical—when it seems to take over my body out of the blue, or emotional—when recalling shameful, sad or hopeless events evokes deep sadness. It is said that depression often springs from thinking about the past while anxiety springs from playing in your head the worst possible outcomes of a situation.

How did my body respond to a depressed mind? I wanted to crawl into a ball on my bed and not move. When it was a mild depression, I still slouched, frowned or had a sad face accompanied by shallow breathing. I wanted to do nothing except dwell in misery. The world lost its appeal and colors. It was too much effort to do anything. Just trying to smile was huge, but it paid off. I was able to begin deep breathing, to cause oxygen to flow through my body. Then I would flex my fingers. That was better than nothing, right? I kept smiling, breathing, and moving fingers. Just staying in bed and smiling was a small step. I began to feel that cure was on the way. I read somewhere about a research where depressed subjects were asked to hold a pencil sideways in their mouths for a few minutes at a time. As a result of activating facial muscles that are used for smiling their mood elevated and depression lifted.

Fear: Friend or Foe?

Most of us are afraid of dying. It causes us to be fearful of accidents, catastrophes, and diseases. At times such fears paralyze us and begin to control our lives, as it happened to me on occasions when I was awaiting test results and battling health issues. Such fears prohibit us from living our lives to the fullest and reaching our God-given potential.

In many cases, experiencing fear is a good thing. Once a child learns that touching a hot or sharp object will hurt, they usually avoid doing that in the future. Being cautious is beneficial. But when does being vigilant become excessive? Where is the line that separates useful fears from becoming obsessive? We know that driving a car can lead to an accident. Does it keep us from ever getting behind a wheel? It did for one of my friends. She never learned to drive a car. Interestingly enough, she didn't have a problem being a passenger and that totally perplexed me, as one can become a victim of an accident regardless of being a driver or a passenger. When she lived in New York, with its extensive public transportation system, this was not an issue, but when her family moved to Southern California, she had to rely on her husband, children or friends to drive her. It became extremely inconvenient, but she never learned to drive.

One of our friends is afraid of flying. He took this fear to an extent that his family never took any vacations that required flying. Did he not hear that it is more likely for a person to die from a car accident than a plane crash?

At what point can fear become obsessive, interfering with the enjoyment of life? When is wearing a facial mask for protection from germs and viruses justifiable and when is it bizarre? Is it better to be open and trusting or extremely cautious and hostile toward strangers?

Do I need to trust my intuition when I sense something is not quite right? I heard a few stories about acting on hunches, which actually saved lives. But how justifiable is it to avoid flying or driving altogether because of fear? Shall we miss out on what this beautiful world has to offer because of our reservations? Is it right to always give in to fear? I don't have answers for others but I had to learn to overcome fears that affect my quality of living. They kept me from enjoying life to the fullest and I didn't like it.

I worked on my fear of flying and saw positive results. As an exercise, I imagined myself as a flight attendant or a pilot. I liked to imagine being a flight attendant who loved her job and I vividly imagined performing my duties as this attendant. I saw in my mind's eyes serving drinks, chatting with my coworkers, joking and laughing. Within a week of such practice my fear significantly diminished.

This can be applied to other fears. Sometimes fears can be overcome within an hour when the correct exercises are chosen and high levels of emotions are applied.

I met many people who were afraid of public speaking, but I remember one story in particular. As a little girl, Jane had to speak in public in a speech meet. She won her school competition and went on to the finals with another teammate. When they arrived at the other school, its unfamiliar surroundings scared her. She became paralyzed with fear. For years since this episode, Jane was afraid to speak in public. She tried, but it always made her feel extremely uncomfortable. A short while ago, when we met, she told me she was trying to fight this fear but it was extremely difficult. I shared with her a technique I learned that helped me tremendously: erasing and replacing memories. The idea is to imagine a particular episode that caused the emotional "hang up" and envision a different, happy scenario instead. Repeating it in your head over and over again will replace the old memory and help rid you of heavy emotional baggage.

I came across the following acronyms: FEAR: False Evidence Appearing Real as well as FEAR: Forget Everything And Run, or: Face Everything And Rise.

Facing My Fears

There were times when overpowering, debilitating fear gripped my whole being and I thought it would never leave. Fear seemed to take over my body and mind during a panic attack. When in the grips of it, I can feel nothing else. I hate even remembering those times—yikes! Everything around me was losing its appeal, even color. I felt as if I was losing my senses and my whole being was dissolving into a gray mush. Everything I enjoyed and held dear didn't matter anymore. It seemed all that was left was despair. Neither beautiful weather nor the things I normally enjoyed doing brought me any satisfaction or joy. I prayed for joy, I prayed for deliverance, but was not getting the results I so desperately longed for. I experienced miracles in my life before and was absolutely positive God would answer my prayers. Why was He so slow to act in this case? I was forlorn from hurt and weary from the darkness around me.

I tried doing everything possible to overcome fear step by step. I created a plan and then exposed myself to the fear triggers. I did it in small doses or imagined what I would do in certain situations, preparing myself. It was an incremental, continuous improvement. This method can be applied to many things, from overcoming fear to establishing a new habit, to learning a new language. Take one little step at a time, then it is not as scary and becomes possible. It really helps to approach any big obstacle or problem by dividing necessary actions into small steps.

Anxiety is a reaction of my body to stress or fear. The amygdala is the fear center of the brain. It is triggered when we are facing great challenge. Our natural reaction is to turn away from what stimulates our fears. Fear of ill health and death, financial disaster, confrontation, loneliness—any of these can paralyze us and take over our mind. I am trying to embrace my fears and face the symptoms of anxiety. It's okay to feel fear, acknowledge its presence in gratitude (it is designed to warn and protect me after all!) and to move forward, with caution if necessary.

Unveiling my deepest fears even to myself is scary in itself, but doing so I may get close to eventually uprooting it for good. I needed to acknowledge my fears and face them in order to eventually conquer them. I wanted to know where they came from, whether they are learned and developed from the experiences and observations of others.

Fighting Fear and the Urge to Control Things

It is a good idea to write fears down on pieces of paper and then burn them. I also can write my worst fears and triggers on a plate with a Sharpie, and then break it! Writing down my fears is helpful, especially separated into two categories: the reasonable and the unreasonable, which things I cannot control and which that I can. My upbringing pushed me into a victim mentality for quite some time, which in turn made me more fearful of possible negative outcomes. I became very good at focusing and dwelling on possible disasters instead of focusing on what I could control and change. I began asking questions: what are the things I can learn from any situation and challenge I face? Could it be that things were predestined and meant to happen in a certain way? How important is it to control things in my life? Can I make peace with the idea that I am unable to control everything and especially anyone? What is the worst possible outcome of a challenge at hand? What is the best possible scenario? After years of focusing on the worst, I finally began imagining the best, not the worst possible outcome.

Finally I realized this: if overwhelming fear is the overpowering force in my life, I can't experience the pure, exuberant joy I wholeheartedly seek. On the other hand, when I fill my heart with gratitude, there is no room for fear, it has to flee—fear and thanksgiving can't coexist in our heart. This is why gratitude brings me joy.

Processing Grief

Unexamined and unprocessed grief can resurface years later at the most inopportune moment, causing emotional turmoil and even physical pain. We need to allow reality to set in and to reflect. We should not try to ignore our feelings or try to move quickly away from these draining feelings. We often need to retrieve in solitude to process, examine and grieve. It came natural to me to block my strong negative emotions. I was uncomfortable and afraid to deal with them. When my father passed away, I was thrown off balance and tried everything to avoid feeling the devastation of this irreplaceable loss. But I did not know how to grieve. We all grieve in different ways, trying to make sense of unbearable loss.

There are ways to process emotions, letting them sink in for a while, to experience them fully right when the cause occurs, preventing them from haunting us later. For many it's very difficult not to dwell in beautiful memories with a person who died. Those memories wash over and then reality hits—the loved one is gone … when a very close and dear family member passes on, it seems impossible to process. Sometimes we need solitude and reflection; sometimes we need to voice our sorrows to a friend or someone who would listen with compassion, not just saying that it is going to be okay because they are uncomfortable with your raw grief. Psychologists and grief counselors are trained to help and guide us through the process.

Even if I viewed grief over the passing of a loved one as justifiable, the loss of a dream I saw as unjustifiable. I tried to block such thoughts even faster. Many different things can evoke feelings of loss and deep sadness. Now I know that regardless of how unjustifiable my emotions of sorrow (or even anger) may seem at first, I need to allow myself to fully feel and process them. Only later I learned to observe and analyze the cause and layers of sadness, feeling the pain fully before letting it go. Grieving and crying over the lost dream is okay. At times I needed the comfort of a few trustworthy friends to listen and pray with me, and also a quiet place to grieve alone. Now I allow myself to fall apart and grieve even over seemingly unimportant things, if they evoke strong emotions. I try to achieve a healthy balance of validating my emotions and eventually letting them go without holding on.

CHAPTER SIX

Mind Games or Breaking the Pattern of Negative Over-thinking

"Worry is a cycle of inefficient thoughts whirling around a center of fear."
Corrie ten Boom

My mind works like a computer, searching for the optimal solution to the situation or task at hand. On any given day, I can think again and again about a to-do list, which shop would have the best prices, in what optimal order I should run ten errands. Worry and fear are learned behaviors that may become a permanent state of mind if not checked. I lived as if all this was the norm, and I know I'm not the only one. Millions of people go through challenges on a daily basis and don't stop and think what's happening, and what causes certain reactions. There are caregivers to aging parents and disabled children, not to mention the prevalent dysfunction in families. Stress, anxiety and depression have become the norm rather than the exception.

There is beauty in the passage in the Gospel of Matthew, where Jesus says not to worry, as God takes care of all, including little birds and delicate flowers. Jesus told people around Him not to worry on numerous occasions, and even gave a command to "stop worrying now." Apostle Paul tells us to worry about nothing but with thanksgiving, present our requests to the Lord. This passage comes from his letter to the Philippians, chapter 4. This is one of my very favorite books in the Bible. Paul was in prison then, but he encouraged his followers to rejoice. I highly recommend you read this letter, as there is such depth and wisdom in it that I need to return to its wisdom again and again, to be reminded of God's mercy and plan for my life. I can dwell in my fears or I can try to find the way to break free.

Worry and Over-Thinking

Many a night I would lay in bed, mind whirling over something, imagining possible outcomes for the problem *du jour*. Disturbing visions of vain imaginations. I would dwell on negative possibilities, letting my mind spin on and on and on. Sound familiar?

I became an expert at whipping myself into a frenzy, and it had to stop, but how? Pesky thoughts sneak in every day. I had to ask myself: what should I allow my mind to lead me to and dwell on? Habitual over-thinking inevitably tightened the grip of fear on my life. It took a long time to learn to block the flood of over-thinking and change the direction of thoughts. It's like slamming a door shut in the face of an unwelcome solicitor and going back to watching a favorite show.

Disturbing Thought Chains

A chain of thought seems to appear from nowhere and its flow is a natural occurrence. For a long time I thought that nothing could be done to pull me out of the destructive, downward spiral of negative thought. Various books taught me otherwise, that with strong desire and tireless practice, I could change the negative flow in an instant. It sounded too good to be true, but it required work that paid off. I concluded that thoughts must be monitored at all times to keep my peace of mind.

A friend suggested to close my eyes and visualize a green apple suspended in the air in a totally dark room lit by a single source of light, like a lamp. Focus on seeing the apple vividly, it's color, the light on its shiny side; try to imagine it spinning slowly in the air, imagine it changing direction of rotation. Another way is to visualize a lit candle. Focus on seeing its color, size, shape, and burning wick. Imagine that every time a disturbing thought enters your conscience, the flame flickers. Try to envision the flame being still. These exercises help to reach the feeling of calm and stop the "mind chatter".

With practice it became possible to interrupt the flood of negativity and to change the direction of my thoughts on most occasions. I had to ask myself: what do I allow my mind to lead me to dwell on? The antidote to habitual over-thinking is a thought-replacing workout. Yes, it is possible to learn to break the chain of negative, disturbing thoughts and replacing them, to change the flow of your thoughts.

Counting My Blessings

Interrupting a flow of negative thoughts and learning to replace them is key. If I am sincerely full of gratitude, I can't possibly be depressed. But how could I have achieved that deep feeling of gratitude if I didn't feel it? Establishing a habit of daily gratitude became the most achievable of all mind games. In the morning I purposed to come up with five things for which I was grateful. I have a beautiful life I know I should feel grateful for, and usually I am. However, it took tremendous effort to feel appreciative when I was overwhelmed with anxiety. Sometimes it was really hard to switch my thinking from my so-called problems to my blessings.

Focusing on Gratitude

Eventually I decided to start my day with a list of five things I was most grateful for, which later morphed into a gratitude journal. I was grateful for the sunshine, for my family and friends, for the conveniences of modern day life. At first I was listing the big things, then, after about a week I was surprised to see what things popped into my head: running water, electricity, my favorite tea, the beauty of a sunset, the smell of a particular flower…

I started a gratitude journal not as another to-do thing to check off my daily list but as a method of emotional survival. Lately I have not written in it but I do mentally count my blessings in the morning. It puts me in the right state of mind, preparing me to face whatever challenges arise.

Gratitude is a very powerful emotion that can negate all the negative ones. I can't be full of love and gratitude and depressed at the same time. Nor can I be angry or anxious; those negative feelings melt away when I truly focus on being grateful. Focusing on gratitude should be a daily practice. It prepares me to face challenges and obstacles and potentially frustrating events that inevitably will appear in life.

Erasing Painful Memories

Some people have blocked memories of trauma, not recalling what happened during robbery, rape, or torture. Our body is protecting us from what we can't yet handle. I heard stories of people who were badly hurt in an accident that felt no pain for hours or days because their bodies released strong painkillers to protect them. There are also reactions in your body when painful memories are imbedded in your conscious mind. What can you do with these painful scenes imbedded in your brain? There is a special technique I call a "memory eraser" that I successfully used to erase and replace the negative memory of a devastating situation. The event that took place at work and triggered the panic response in my body haunted me for quite some time. Imagining a room and a meeting that took place there, where I felt attacked and not protected was very painful and threw me into emotional turmoil time after time. I was determined to diminish if not eliminate the power its memory had over me. Imagine how excited I was when I was able to achieve both!

I envisioned this event, pretending to be an outside observer, watching events unfold as if in a movie theatre on a screen. I imagined sitting in a comfortable chair, with a bucket of popcorn in my lap, just watching a movie with a remote in my hand. I could see everyone present in the scene, including myself, but from a distance. I was watching the scene unfolding on a screen in front of me, and as soon as it became too painful to watch, I "pressed" the "rewind" button on my imaginary remote. I would "see" all the characters in the scene to move backwards, as if I was really playing the tape backwards. When I rewind to the beginning, I will "play" it again, this time making characters move faster, remembering that I am just an observer, I see myself on the screen only as a character. Backward again I go.

Next time I play my "movie" I add the colors and loud fun sounds, like at the carnival. Now I would have fun with my characters. It is the same scene, but I see myself as a puppeteer now, imagining strings on character's limbs, I can move them anyway I want. I "rewind" the "movie" a few times, making it totally silly and funny every time I run it true, with all the bright colors, music and carnival atmosphere- playing it in fast mode is the best. I might need to return to this exercise a few times, but with every painful situation I used it for, the results were amazing—when I try to remember it, the memory becomes distorted by the fun colorful "movie" I created!

Scheduling My Week vs. Eliminating To-Do Lists

It is easy to get overwhelmed when you have a mile-long to-do list. It all needs to be done, but is it possible to do it all? When you have a list from which you cross off things you accomplished, does it make you feel good? I am sure it does. Here is another question then: how does it make you feel when you have lots of things uncrossed or unchecked on your list at the end of a day? What do you do? Do you copy unfinished tasks to the next day or stay up late to finish them all? Does everything on your list have to be done by you? Can you delegate or maybe prioritize and forget the rest? When I had a tendency to get extremely overwhelmed by the simplest tasks due to anxiety disorder, I began implementing a Rule of Three: no more than three errands in a row. I had to do this to stop my mind from going into an overdrive.

When I had a long list of things to be done, I had paralyzing bouts of anxiety. To fight it, I radically prioritized and cut all errands in chunks of three. I could go to a bank, grocery store and a post office, let's say, and everything else had to wait or be delegated. Asking others to do things for me was not easy. First, there still was this "residue" of perfectionism: nobody can do it better than I. Second, a fear of rejection that may come when I try to delegate and ask others to do things for me. How many women avoid asking their family members to do things for fear of getting a stare, a complaint or something worse? Just wondering?

Later on, when I felt strong enough to do more, I still prioritize what needs to be done first, what can be eliminated and what tasks I shall delegate. It helps to plan a whole week ahead, grouping tasks as home and family, work, spiritual growth and church activities, health and wellness, friends, etc. One curious example of my new efficiency is to avoid running long-distance errands on Tuesdays, if possible. I realized that major stores are being restocked on this day and I noticed more trucks on the road.

Focusing On The Present

I am less prone to stress when I focus on the moment. One of the ways to do it is to become aware of my body. If I am sitting, I think about how my body feels on the chair, feet planted on the ground. I can move my fingers and wiggle my toes. Doing so helps to distract my brain from whatever problem—real or imaginary—I might be dwelling on.

Matters of the Heart

Why do I feel heavy emotions as a physical sensation in the heart? Anxiety is often felt in the middle of the chest. Is it actually my heart that hurts when I feel something deeply? Why do I feel the "stab in the chest" sensation when in heavy emotional turmoil? When burdened with problems we are said to have a heavy heart, when experiencing grief and sorrow we have a broken heart, in betrayal our heart is being wounded, when dealing with relationship problems it is a heart that aches...

How can I fill my heart with peace and love?

With eyes closed and one or both hands in the middle of the chest area, I straighten up and take deep breaths. I imagine filling my heart with love and gratitude. After a short while, pain decreases and goes away. Gratitude and love ultimately negate worries, fear and anxiety.

Surroundings

Beautiful sunny beaches of California are not the places we associate with anxiety or depression. How pathetic is it to be lying on a beautiful beach in Malibu, sulking? But there I was, surrounded by sun–soaked beauty, looking at the shimmering blue waves and still feeling as if in a thick cloud of despair...I was trying to be grateful but it was hard to feel true gratitude. I wished with sadness to be able to receive an answer to my prayers on the spot and to be well again.

It does not matter where you live or how seemingly perfect your life might seem from the outside. I think that is why so many people are hooked on reality TV shows about celebrities and wealthy people—they all have problems and issues! To me, despair and powerlessness occurred no matter where I was. These feelings just came over me like a wave, drowning all my joy. If I was living in a cold climate with long winters, I could have blamed my foul mood on lack of daylight, but that was not the case. Neither a beautiful vacation-like setting nor the perpetual sunshine was able to dissolve symptoms of anxiety and depression. It made me feel ridiculous at times because so many people are suffering while living in poor conditions. It didn't matter where I lived and what my surroundings were. Depression and anxiety strike regardless of the beautiful backdrop. Changing scenery or going away for a while proved to be just a temporary fix. I needed to get to the bottom of the problem. With the help of mental-care professionals and self-education, I was able to do just that. It was a rather long process, even though I was able to shorten it significantly with persistence and drive.

CHAPTER SEVEN

Expecting The Tide to Turn

*"He will yet fill your mouth with laughter
and your lips with shouts of joy."*
Job 8:21

Adrenalin rush

People who seek scary, thrilling sports and activities are often referred to as "adrenaline junkies." For many, it becomes a true addiction. Once "hooked," these thrill-seekers will travel thousands of miles to catch the biggest waves, ski from the highest mountains, jump from airplanes, bridges, and buildings... they seek activities that trigger the release of adrenaline into their bloodstreams. After watching a program on TV that focused on such people's stories, I often wondered: what pushes them to seek these experiences again and again? I could not relate...

Living in Paradise Cove, an amazing place in Malibu known for its surf, did not motivate me to try this sport. I love to swim but the cold water of the Pacific Ocean kept me on the shore most of the time, even during the summer. As I walked on the beach, I watched surfers riding the waves in all kinds of weather condition: from gorgeous sunny days with gentle waves to stormy days and twelve-foot waves. Only a few ventured into surf when the waves resembled multi-story buildings, but those who practiced for years mastered riding the waves and fully enjoy the thrill of subduing the elements.

Anxiety can wash over as a huge, powerful and frightening wave. It is impossible to avoid waves in the ocean, and when they get extremely big it gets pretty scary. Surfers learn the patterns of the ocean currents, and for accomplished surfers, riding even the biggest swells becomes a thrilling ride. I thought that maybe I could utilize the adrenaline rush I experience during an anxiety attack and turn it into something if not pleasurable than at least not as scary.

As I was not a surfer, I thought to find another activity I can do or even imagine that will give me positive reaction to adrenaline release. I thought of watching thrillers, riding a rollercoaster or driving fast on a track, but found it in skiing. I am not an avid skier, but I can remember the thrill of going down the slopes, surrounded by the beauty of snow-covered trees, breathing the crisp mountain air. Even if I am not there, I can still imagine it. I tried it a few times when anxiety washed over: closed my eyes and imagined riding down the mountain. To my great relief, it worked. So I got another anxiety fighting, or rather in this case anxiety-utilizing tool.

As I learned what anxiety is about, what may trigger it and how I can deal with it, this adversary became less and less scary, but rather annoying.

Self-education

I had a deep desire to get well and was willing to do anything to be set free of anxiety. Switching my brain into constructive mode in the midst of immense pain was hard, but I discovered that recovery begins with the strong desire and will to get the victory. I was determined to get well and it drove me to action. I had to become proactive on my way to healing—I did not see any other way. I couldn't just sit and wait for a magic cure.

I would go to bookstores and a local library to get as many books on anxiety disorders as possible. Reading them was not an easy task because, without fail, the reading triggered the symptoms of acute panic attack. Almost every page I read reminded me of the worst I'd been through. Just picking up such a book would give me severe physical symptoms of anxiety. It made me want to throw it away, crawl into a ball and wait for the pain to dissipate. Sometimes I did just that, taking time to recuperate. I knew I wasn't going to die and that those symptoms, painful as they were, were just the body's reaction to perceived but non-existent danger. Eventually, my persistence would take over and I continued to battle through reading and learning, eventually to be victorious.

From books I learned that children who had to grow up fast, tending to their family, are likely to have panic attacks when they grow up. Usually it would be the oldest child in a family. There was a lot of information on the connection between perfectionism and anxiety, diet and anxiety, as well as other triggers and predispositions. I am extremely grateful that I liked research and learning, as it served me and empowered me.

Various Specialists

At the very beginning of this whole ordeal, the first symptom I had was tightness in my shoulders and neck. I thought it was logical to see a chiropractor. I experienced some relief after a few sessions, but not completely. In a few days, I felt tightness in my chest and some numbness down my left arm. When these symptoms persisted and even worsened I thought I'd better see a cardiologist, which I did. After numerous tests, I was assured my symptoms were not due to a major heart problem and was relieved. Doctors found some abnormality, but I was in no danger and didn't even need medication for the heart condition I had. It put me somewhat at ease, but I was still suffering a great deal. My anxiety was much more than nervousness in stressful situations and I sought qualified professionals with whom I was comfortable talking and whom

I trusted. I believe in seeking second or third opinions and even changing healthcare providers if something didn't feel right. My health was my responsibility and even though I often felt totally out of control in my own body, I pushed through, looking for cure. Over time, I assembled a healing team of various specialists.

I was in the care of my family physician, seeing a psychologist and was evaluated by a psychiatrist for disability. I believe far too many people are living in denial, afraid to admit there is anything wrong with them, thus refusing to seek help. What if they go to see a doctor and get a diagnosis of a disturbing mental illness? In this information age, way too many people suffer for fear of the unknown. Admittedly, facing inner demons is scary; it is so much easier to do nothing, not forcing yourself to be brave and fight even if the possible outcome is wellbeing and happiness.

An old joke comes to mind about a guy drowning in a river. God sends him a boat, a raft and a log, but the man refuses help, waiting for His divine intervention. When this man finally drowned and went to heaven, he asked God why He did not rescue him. Then God answered: who do you think sent your way all those floating devices you so foolishly refused?! This can illustrate that when we look for healing, God sends doctors, other health care providers, medication, and psychologists to help us when needed.

Psychological Help

Though I was glad to be diagnosed early on, I was not ecstatic to learn that I had panic disorder, as I had not yet been free of the idea of stigma. I was clinging to the secondary diagnosis of mild heart condition, using it initially as the apparent cause of my hospitalization to family and friends.

I am so glad I didn't have to be admitted to a hospital for mental patients. I had a fleeting suicidal thought, which disappeared, thankfully, not to come back. Years ago, my close relative had to spend a few weeks at the psychiatric ward and I was told it was a horrible experience. It was a different country and different time, but even in beautiful California, being admitted to a mental institution is not something to brag about and nothing to look forward to. With mental disorders so prevalent now, the stigma becomes less and less. But at that time, I was burning with shame when I was not able to return to work, but greatly relieved to know that the only time I was admitted to a hospital was at the very beginning, when my heart had to be checked. I was also grateful that I could use a mild heart condition as my excuse for not returning to teaching. I was a total mess inside, yet for a while I concealed it in conversations, even with close friends, because I was painfully ashamed.

Many people turn to psychologists as a last resort, the same way they wait until the bitter end to seek specialists in other areas of life: finances, marriage, life choices etc. There are caring and highly educated people who specialize in all issues of relationship and mental health. This type of expense should be categorized as a necessity, similar to health, dental, house and auto maintenance.

As so many others with emotional and physical distress, I was not yet convinced I needed to see a psychologist, but was forced, due to absence from work. This turned out in my favor, so I'm glad I did it early on. The first psychologist lent me a book and CD with exercises for overcoming panic. I followed the recommendations as was prescribed. The only exercise I remember is drawing an imaginary circle on the floor around me to feel protected. At first it sounded bizarre, but I gave it a try. I was determined to try even the silly or flat out crazy. And if such advice was found in a book written by a distinguished Ph.D., it only strengthened my resolve to submit. Drawing those imaginary circles around me on the bathroom floor sounded almost pagan, but it did indeed give me a strange feeling of being sheltered and protected, and I know they were designed to represent the boundary of protection from the outside world. Later I read about using a hula-hoop to create a similar boundary. In any case, creating these circles was beneficial for someone who thought she was completely losing her mind. It was a temporary fix because I felt I was a total mess.

My first therapist was very nice, but specialized in family and marriage counseling. By the time of my last insurance-covered visit, I was nowhere near being well, so I looked up an anxiety specialist. With the help of my physician, I got a list of my insurance providers, narrowed it down to my preference of female specialists in the area and checked references. I chose a psychologist I thought best to address my needs and made my first appointment. I was prepared to see a few psychologists from my list to choose the one I was the most comfortable with—after all, during therapy sessions, I would bare my very soul and unearth many deeply hidden issues I told no one about. I was relieved that I felt comfortable with the very first anxiety specialist I saw. I stayed in therapy for almost a year and it was very helpful. During those sessions, long-repressed thoughts and experiences gushed from me as streams of cleansing water, verbalized for the first time. They trickled at first, then the floodgates opened and I wept, fully experiencing relief. In the past, when painful events happened, I didn't allow myself to properly grieve, shoving all the emotions deep inside, covering them with a veneer of "I don't give a damn" attitude. Obviously, that backfired. Talking to a mental care professional met a need to express my thoughts and emotions in confidence, but with the realization that I am not my thoughts and feelings, I only experience them, which was very helpful.

After a while, I was telling my therapist that I would like to find a life coach. I wanted to create sort of an action plan for my future and move forward faster. Though life coaching not her specialty, she helped me by providing what she was trained to do: listening as I spilled my emotions and pain, guiding me to open up and look for emotional patterns in my stories, bringing me to realization what in many instances was holding me back.

When I think I am sick with an ear infection, severe stomachache or flu, I go straight to the doctor's office, describe my symptoms and expect to be treated. Once properly diagnosed, anxiety, as well as depression and anger, are as treatable and curable as other diseases.

Unfortunately, I am addicted to instant gratification. If not all of us, definitely a majority of us want immediate healing. Unfortunately, healing takes time and there is no magic pill that could cure me completely and on the spot. There are drugs to make me feel better instantly (halleluiah!) by changing my biochemistry in a matter of minutes. The first few times I took it, the effect felt good. But I didn't want to get addicted to pills (or anything else). Also, the emotional numbness and fog made me avoid long-term medication, so I used them only as a last resort. I kept them in my purse and just knowing that I can take them was like a safety net, though this was not a long-term solution.

I respected my doctor's opinions but I wanted to fully participate in the healing process. It was my responsibility to choose the treatment that I was comfortable with. I turned to many health care providers, but I was also doing my homework.

By working with psychologists, I learned to ask myself deep questions and to discover motives for my fears, longings and other emotions. When I ponder a question for a while, I can come with an answer. It usually wells up inside and comes out with tears. I was wondering why on many occasions I was thinking about leaving my home church I was a member of for over a decade. The answer emerged and I felt very sad and emotional, I know... I was longing for stability and belonging for a very long time. Our little church in Malibu is a very nice place but it went through numerous transitions. People come and go. When I come in now I hardly see any familiar faces. I became an expert of asking the right questions to figure out roots of my internal conflicts. I can even help those close to me to figure out what really bothers them.

Desperate Need of Self-Care

Juggling a career, a household with its endless errands and chores at times leave me feel tired, unlovable and even resentful. Without taking care of myself, I am often unable to care for my beloved family and people close to me the way I truly want. Long gone are times when I tried to manipulate others to pity me; now I learn to delegate. When "my glass is empty," I can't share "living water" of my life with others. I need to take time to fill up. The best way to do it is to spend time in being still in God's presence. Reading the Scriptures, praying and listening in silence are necessary and refreshing to soul, mind and body. We need to allot uninterrupted time for this purpose without feeling guilty that we are not productive.

There are also days when I simply need to stay in my pajamas, watch old movies and eat comfort food. Then there are days when I can eat salads, go for a walk or work out and organize my drawers and closets. Both ways can help to refocus and recharge batteries. I want to mention that we need to be aware when problem avoidance and escapism lasts for months and we become reluctant, lazy or afraid to venture into the real world. So a plan should be developed to get out of this vicious circle of despondency, depression and lethargy. There is a way to live fully, moving forward in a healthy pace.

We all need to seek balance in our lives. Self-care is necessary, using simple antidotes: down-time with a magazine or a book, a silly comedy or a little sketch on YouTube, a walk or a run, face-to-face time with girlfriends, or just a phone chat. When I am really pressed on time but I need this "girl time". I may have a cup of coffee with a girlfriend on Skype or Face Time, wearing my pajamas. Hooray for technology! Sometimes, when the pile-up of things to do gets too much and life seems to be spinning out of control, extreme self-care measures need to be scheduled and implemented, even if it seems there is no time. Women especially often feel guilty for not being productive or being selfish in taking care of themselves. Occasionally it'll take a drastic measure of scheduling a massage, a haircut or manicure, an adults-only dinner or a trip—all the good stuff. It does not have to be expensive; there are ways to barter goods and services with other women in my circle. Where there's a will, there's a way—proven!

The Art of Waiting and Resting

You may not expect a life coach to recommend waiting; after all, coaching is about taking action, completing tasks and beating procrastination. Sure, taking action is important, but there are times when we need to pause and compose ourselves before taking a leap. I learned the hard way the importance of rest, but I can be a slow learner, and my God, my teacher used whatever methods He saw fit. He Himself took a break after creating the world. That should've been a clue, but of course, I didn't learn from somebody else's example, silly me! God chose to take this time off and actually commanded us to have such a day of complete rest -- doing nothing for a day, on a weekly basis. Jesus, after preaching, healing and ministering, had to withdraw to have a time of reflection, prayer and solitude. I had to learn the importance of this practice, but not at once. I was anxious and frustrated, wondering why I was not able to shake off darkness that seemed to cling on and blind me. I wanted to move forward and find out what to do next. Last thing I wanted to do was to lay dormant and wait. But I had to hang on and reflect at first, learning patience from God's Creation. All kinds of analogies resurfaced to teach me.

A seed goes into the ground to die as a seed and to grow into a daisy, a head of cabbage or a mighty oak, but if you don't know what kind of seed you are planting, you will not know what to expect. From a tiny seed that you can barely see, a huge tree can eventually grow, given proper care and conditions. A caterpillar eats leaves, grows bigger and bigger, then it makes a cocoon around itself, where it undergoes metamorphosis, being totally transformed while hidden from view, to emerge in due time as a beautiful butterfly. We only have to wait and see. None of us know for sure how our lives will turn out, but those times come when we need to go into complete stillness, hidden from the eyes of others, to undergo complete transformation, and to emerge as an entirely new creation.

A time of solitude was, after all, necessary for my growth. But after a while, it felt like prison. I got very tired of being dormant.

It took time for me to break through my "cocoon." Eventually I did spread my wings and found that I can fly. Another way to look at it is that I had to slowly emerge and grow from the darkness, as a vine trying to hold onto anything within reach for support, but inevitably growing stronger and taller, reaching for the sun.

CHAPTER EIGHT

Coping Mechanisms

"We are certainly in a common class with the beasts;
every action of animal life is concerned with seeking bodily
pleasure and avoiding pain."
St. Augustine

Similar to our primitive fight or flight response to imminent danger is our instinct to seek pleasure and to avoid pain.

Are Distractions Good For Me?

So called "timewasters" are often used to escape and avoid pain: mindless shopping, frivolous reading, watching pointless shows all can fall in this category. A long time ago, I thought I should be ashamed of myself for even going there, trying to run away from fears, not facing life challenges head on, caving in and attempting to escape stress… I used to think this way before I was hit with debilitating anxiety. That is when the game plan had to change. I had to get well before I was to re-learn to set powerful goals, achieve and strive. For the time being, my biggest goal was to get out of pain and despair, using whatever I could in trial and error.

I realized it's okay to sometimes just indulge in relaxing activities that don't need to be productive. At times I would break the cycle of over-thinking and remedy my pity party by watching a comedy show, a funny movie or funny clips on the Internet or TV. Shopping mindlessly for nothing in particular lifted my mood on occasion. Thankfully, I usually stuck with shopping at Ninety-Nine Cents or discount stores or browsed the food stores. This way it did not affect my pocket book too much and was even cheaper than seeing a therapist. I was buying myself some distractions, on a budget.

Reading novels also helped me to get my mind off what was bothering me and block the over-thinking. Curling up on a couch with an interesting book was a perfect way to escape. A good novel made stress and anxiety melt away. It still does. I like reading for education but I read for fun as well and it does not have to be serious literature. Similarly, what I watch on TV does not have to be educational or inspirational. From time to time I can just sit on the couch and watch two or three movies in a row and I am totally Okay with that. It's therapy, baby!

Self-medicating to Escape Pain

Many people self-medicate, using anything possible to get rid of pain. We can use shopping, TV, or reading to distract us from reality. A reasonable amount is helpful. When we are trying to escape problems, physical or emotional pain by using alcohol, food, gambling, or social media, we must beware of addiction.

There is a widespread issue about self-medicating with legal and illegal substances, including alcohol. Wine became a quick remedy and a drug of choice. It helped me to suppress anxiety and negative feelings, and it dulled senses and pain. It never provided a cure, only temporary relief and a break from pain. Using wine as an anti-anxiety remedy was tricky because one glass of wine was helpful in relaxing me, but more than that would wake me up in the middle of the night, causing even more anxiety. Using alcohol to numb one's senses is totally different from enjoying a glass of fine wine with a good meal, savoring it drop by drop. It definitely was not a remedy for constant stress and anxiety I was experiencing. I could not drink every night to ease pain out of concern of making things worse, or becoming an alcoholic.

Hypochondria: True Health Issues and "Imaginary Maladies"

Listening to what my body says helps to catch symptoms early and avoid potential problems. I understand when pains and aches are caused by anxiety and when there's a true health issue. The majority of true issues are, as you would guess, caused by stress. Welcome to the vicious circle, the merry-go-round of stress. They say that the most heart attacks occur on Monday. That's when many of us face yet another stressful week at work.

It often is a great challenge to discern if illness is real or imaginary. Same goes about fears. I learned not to be afraid of chest pain when it was not caused by a life-threatening heart problem.

In the field of hypochondria I am, yet again, an overachiever. As a matter of fact, I consider myself a hypochondriac extraordinaire.

As I moved along this winding road to healing, I became my own guinea pig. Again and again, various real and perceived health issues stopped me in my track. I would lie in bed or move around, fearful, my attention occupied with the only problem that seemed important at the time—what is wrong with me and how to get well. It took close to a decade of personal research to understand how my mind-body connection works. I want to achieve health and strength, stamina to endure anything life brings. I also am striving to cultivate the joy of healthy, fulfilled living.

Self-importance and Self-pity

It is fascinating to me, but some people, either consciously or unconsciously, don't want to get well. Fighting to get well is hard, and not everybody wants to do the work. It is easier to label oneself as clinically this-or-that and carry it as a flag—look at me, I have a diagnosis that is bigger than yours. I came across a few types of people with mental conditions: some are battling to get better at all cost, and fast. Then there are others who are afraid to speak about it and suffer in isolation, not getting the help needed. And then there is another group that has been going from doctor to doctor to hear that there is something wrong and this becomes twisted into a sense of self-importance. For years I belonged to the latter group...

If you tell a chronic hypochondriac that there may be a simple solution to his problem, he would not believe you because his problems are important to him. Have you ever heard people comparing their diseases as if they were prized possessions? If such a person got cured on the spot, what is left of their self-importance? Perhaps they will turn to discovering their true life's purpose, but for now they have a counterfeit purpose of being sick.

The longer I felt sorry for myself, the deeper I spiraled into a despised depression. I longed to be vibrant again. Getting sympathy was comforting but it wasn't the key.

Then I would hear a story like that of Monica George, who went to a hospital to deliver a baby through a C-section. While there, she contracted a flesh-eating bacteria, and both her legs and arms had to be amputated. Who could have blamed her if she fell into despair? But having two daughters at home, Monica decided to be a role model for overcoming obstacles. She is an incredible example to all of rising above horrible circumstances.

Then there is Nick Vujicic, who was born without limbs. Far from stopping his life, he became a motivational speaker, author, businessman, husband and father. I had the privilege of hearing him speak in person a few times and was moved to the core with his mountain-moving faith in God.

Not long ago I also was honored to meet Joni Eareckson Tada. She became a quadriplegic at seventeen as a result of a diving accident, but her life did not end there. This strong and courageous woman founded Joni and Friends International Disability Center and became a world-renowned advocate for those who are disabled. She learned to write and even paint by holding a pen or a paintbrush between her teeth. She has written close to fifty inspiring books. She survived breast cancer. She got married *after* her accident. She travels the world speaking and raising awareness of needs of those with disabilities. She is a member of the Disability Advisory Committee of the U.S. State Department. She is a radio host. Yet for almost fifty years she has been paralyzed from the shoulders down. She needs to be turned over during every night, she needs help with eating and drinking. In the morning she relies on the help of others to get ready for her busy day. It takes close to two hours to get her ready… yet she loves her God with all her heart and worships Him with her words, actions and songs!

Whenever I am tempted to feel sorry for myself, all I need to do is watch an inspirational video about these people or read one of their books and the cure is guaranteed. If they were able to overcome seemingly insurmountable obstacles, so can I. My God can give each of us strength and courage. We only need to seek it as it is much easier to dwell in misery.

Making a Difference

Depression, worry and anxiety are ultimately very selfish feeling: how does life's events and challenges make *me* feel? Love, compassion and servitude are focusing on others or focusing on appreciation. I need to examine my emotions, but then, ultimately I must switch to contributing.

When I feel down, I need to reach out to someone. It may be a person on my prayer list, a friend who is going through tough times and needs encouragement. Or I may offer a prayer for someone without even talking to them, or just sending a text that that person is in my thoughts and prayers. Anything to get my mind off *me*.

Reading or watching stories of people overcoming tragedy is powerful and encouraging. Taking action to help those in greater need than myself is even more powerful and healing. There's always a way to find those who need my help and act on it. It sure will shift my focus from me and my problems to being of service to those who need me. My dear friends exemplified to me serving others with open hearts. My friend Roni volunteered at delivering meals to the elderly and walked dogs at the local animal shelter. Larisa gives of her time at a free clinic in her area. Than there is a Prison Ministry where my friends share the hope of the Gospel with those who needs to hear it weekly.

Love of the Family

Our families need our love and attention as well. They also can be the best supporters and cheerleaders, as were my amazing husband and son. There was no manual given to my family members on how to cope with mental illness of their loved one. My husband was very supportive and kind, but I knew it was very hard for him to witness my pain without the ability to remove it and protect me. He would love to be able to wipe it out completely and make me instantly well, but that was not happening. Men are natural problem-solvers and to helplessly watch their ladies suffer can make them undergo emotional turmoil as well.

After my teenage son realized what was going on with me, he began treating me like a fragile china doll. I know I was not looking or acting myself on many occasions and it must have affected him deeply. But he was there for me, being very loving, kind and protective. He tried to do his best not to worry me and, for a teenager, it was a challenge to be on his best behavior at all times.

Oxycuddling!

It is proven by science that when we hug or cuddle, we produce oxytocin, a hormone sometimes referred to as a "bonding' or "love" hormone, because when we kiss or hold a loved one, the levels rise. It is known to bond a person to a newborn child or a person we love.

When an overwhelming cloud of emotional darkness and despair was hanging over me, hugging my family members instantly elevated my mood. When it was extremely difficult, my sweet husband or son would give me long hugs, and that worked miracles. It was so comforting that often we embraced for a long time because I didn't want them to let go. After such hugs, I felt much better. To this day, we still hug often, as we all realized how good it makes us feel. We even joke about it. "I need my oxytocin!" is a code for a bear hug.

Pooch Therapy

Production of feel-good hormones by the body may be caused not only with human touch. Petting a dog or a cat has a similar effect—there is hope to feel good to those single people out there. Pets of all sorts: bunnies, horses, birds and even reptiles all provided comfort and helped my friends to feel better when they were stressed.

Actually, in my case, even just looking at my dog lying on a couch in the middle of the day-- legs out, total peace in all her little body, I can't help but smile. How does she do it? Shouldn't she be worrying about what she will have for dinner or what that poodle down the street thought about her uncombed coat this morning? Silly, right? Who cares! She is not ashamed or concerned about how she looks when running on the beach. She's self-confident, regardless of what size dog she encounters, while she is a tiny little Pomeranian. Why then do I worry about things that are similarly irrelevant?

Positive Friends

Spending time with cheerful dogs and with upbeat, optimistic people elevates my mood. A good mood as well as a bad one is contagious.

I have to admit: on occasion I just need my "down" time to be alone. That is how I recharge. There were also times when it felt good to have a pity-party and complain to anyone who would listen about how miserable I was. What I realized is that doing this for long only prolonged the blues. Talking about problems and misery can become a competition—whose life is worse… I've done that too and it did not serve me well.

I need to surround myself with bubbly, uplifting, encouraging friends, otherwise I become drained. Having an uplifting, humorous, or deep conversation with a dear friend is refreshing, especially the one who "gets" me. If this person prays with me and for me it brings it to a different level altogether. Just chatting for a while with someone I love and trust restores my energy and distracts me or helps to have a different perspective on things. Even texting or checking on friends on social media helps me feel connected. Studies show that being a part of a community and feeling encouraged increases the levels of the mood-elevating hormones dopamine and serotonin.

Creative Visualization or Instant Vacation

When I was a child, I had no problem making a "cake" in a sandbox and then happily "eating" it with my friends. I played with imaginary objects and often found refuge in the make-believe world. I realize I can still fantasize and use it to my advantage. Imagination is one of the keys to overcome negative emotions. Daydreaming and visualizing are key to experiencing the freedom of a childlike nature. What do you miss the most from being five years old? For me it's simply the freedom of dreaming again!

Visualization is a powerful technique and is often used by psychologists. But it was hard to envision myself on a quiet beach in the Caribbean when my heart was beating what felt like a thousand beats a minute. It was possible to calm down, but took too much time and effort. A few years ago, I took my first snow skiing lesson. Please don't laugh, but this girl who was raised in Ukraine with its cold snowy winters only learned to ski cross-country over there. It took years and a move to California to be introduced to mountain skiing. My first experience was so much fun! I didn't go beyond the bunny slopes, but even with only that, I now had one more trick up my sleeve to utilize the adrenaline rush when anxiety attacks.

Was there ever an activity that you enjoyed doing that gave you the pleasant rush of adrenaline? Imagine yourself in that scenario when panic or anger strikes. I resorted to imagining myself on a slope, overlooking a beautiful snow-covered valley with breathtaking mountains. I would even put my hands in front of me as if holding the poles and sway my torso a little. My breathing became even and washed away the anxiety. Just imagining myself skiing instantly relaxed me.

I also came up with this visualization of the word "Love." There is something about this word that casts out anxiety and fear. It is simply magical.

Guided imagery often has well-proven therapeutic effect. But there is also healing in looking at the beauty of nature. It usually didn't work for me on the spot, especially in the case of acute anxiety, which accumulated over time. Taking time to go for a nature walk and literally smell the roses is restorative. I don't need to live in the suburbs or close to nature to benefit from this. When I lived in the city I would go for a walk in the park. Visiting art museums had a similar positive effect.

I love to travel but I can't travel all the time. What I can do is dream about far-away places as often as I like. I like to imagine being on a secluded tropical island, ocean waves lazily licking white sand under picturesque palm trees. Unbelievably bright blue sea, shimmering in the sun… branches swaying gently in a light breeze that wafts the aroma of tropical flowers… paradise can be conjured just by closing my eyes. The key is to employ all my senses: hear the ocean and seagulls, smell the ocean and flowers, feel the sand under my feet, see the vibrant tropical colors… It is very relaxing and can help me to relax or go to sleep.

One of the ways to boost relaxing visualization is to look at a picture in a magazine or on the Internet, one that brings a sense of tranquility and a smile. I would look at it for a few minutes while breathing deeply and fully. Most comforting and relaxing for me are photos of tropical beaches, snow-covered majestic mountains, vacation destinations, nature and flowers or cute puppies. Another sure temporary fix for me is finding pictures or videos of cute pets, especially Pomeranian puppies, on the Internet. These cute little fluff balls inevitably put a smile on my face.

Gardening as Therapy

I love to garden as a hobby and as a form of exercise. Watching things grow, nurturing them and then enjoying the fruit of my labor—quite literally—brings me joy. Over the years I realized that a perfectionist couldn't make a joyful gardener. Growing plants depends on too many factors. We cannot put pressure on God to grow things overnight. We attempt to speed up the process by fertilizing, adding good soil and water, but in the end we are not in control of the growing process. We need patience after the planting is done, to watch, wait, weed, water, and wait some more. I never thought about it in-depth, but gardening taught me patience.

Benefit of Hobbies

Menial hobbies, just like gardening, have a calming effect on many people. Cross-stitching, knitting difficult patterns or putting puzzles together shifts my focus and it is a sure way to clear out many mental cobwebs, which seem to just dissolve. Exploring a new hobby will help to break the pattern of thought compulsion and open a brain path of creativity.

Working on a thousand-piece puzzle instantly shifts my attention to a task at hand. I can't think of anything else but the intricate pattern being worked on. When I count the cross-stitching or am knitting a complicated pattern, I become engrossed and therefore liberated. I know not everyone can relate. Some people would be frustrated in a matter of minutes, but lucky for me it has the opposite effect, and so it is now my go-to thought-diversion tool.

Aside from working on complicated patterns, there is another rather unusual activity that keeps me calm. I'm one of those rare people who like doing dishes by hand. Warm soapy water just reminds of a bubble bath; running water splashing peacefully like a fountain.

Handiwork like knitting, crocheting or scrapbooking, because of its repetitiveness, puts us in a light state, similar to meditation, which interferes with the production of stress hormones. I was knitting and crocheting up a storm when I was not reading. Making scarves for charity helped me even more with the comfort of helping others. Choose a hobby if you don't have one and be sure it's right for you. I like knitting, crocheting and gardening (which doubles as exercise). I even learned a few crotchet patterns from You Tube!

Reading

Not many things can relax me better than reading a good mystery novel by my favorite author while lying on a couch or in bed. When this is accompanied by a cup of hot tea and a snack, immediate problems disappear. These are ways to refocus and unwind and this particular one is my favorite. It does not require much preparation. Of course, if a quiet place is not available, then I move onto something else.

I love to read, but when I got ill, I was no longer enjoying serious literature. Reading books or listening to tapes on anxiety usually brought all my symptoms back. It was quite a dilemma: should I study my "enemy" (anxiety disorder) or get lost in a good book? Though I set out to learn about my disease and conquer it, it was too painful to read about it, so I got hooked on light mystery books. Distraction is a useful tool and I put it to good use.

Reading books for pleasure or thumbing through magazines can put the brakes on suffering. The overachiever in me nagged that I have to read serious books and be productive, which used to lead me straight to insanity. No more! I will grab my beach "read" to unwind, recuperate and give my mind a much-needed break. Reading without concentrating on what I've read, not analyzing, sometimes even not being able to recall some scenes or names of characters—its all right with me now. I am not writing a dissertation, I just need a temporary diversion from obligations, chores and to-do lists.

I have dozens of books at home that sat for years, unread. I want to remind you that I am a "bookaholic"...

Change Habits

Repetitive, habitual thought patterns wear a groove in the brain that can be changed, like lifting the needle from a record, for those who remember vinyl records. My old way of thinking was also a habit. It was time to establish a new one, to re-record the tape that plays in my head.

Nowadays, when the over-thinking tries to come over me, most of the time I am able to stop it right then and there without allowing it to get a foothold in my brain. I examine what my white-knuckle fears could be and how I could trade them in for confidence. Of course, I am talking about unreasonable or vaguely reasonable fears. I can drive myself crazy over so many things!

Driving

A person who's had a car accident will often have driving anxiety, even by watching a crash scene in a movie. The very thought of driving triggers major anxiety in some people.

What if I get anxiety while driving a car? I do get nervous driving through a canyon at night in rain, when the rocks are falling off the cliffs. As I mentioned, I had an accident under such conditions. To reduce fear, I visualized the destination of my trip, usually home, where my family would greet me before having a pleasant evening together. I relaxed at the wheel; no longer white-knuckling it.

Have you ever driven with windows down, music blasting, singing at the top of your lungs? If not, try it—it's very freeing. It took me a few tries because I am normally so reserved; now I'm like a rock star at the wheel.

Listening to CDs in My Car/ Mobile Education

My commute through the canyon that connects Malibu with Conejo Valley to go to work or to run errands took on average half an hour one way. The breathtaking beauty of it inspired daily prayer. I also liked listening to music. High in the mountains, radio reception was quite sketchy, so I had to use CDs. I like various kinds of music, singing along to upbeat tunes one day and on another choosing calming music that at times helped to slow down my heart rate and lower blood pressure. When in distress, I was reminded of the story of King Saul. When he was overcome by demons, he would call David to sing and play his harp to calm him down.

Over time, I switched to listening to educational and spiritual teachings on CDs. They provided a welcomed distraction from disturbing thoughts that popped up in my head without an invitation. I found many teachings available through the local library and regularly checked out new ones. Listening to them helped me to focus on healing and gave hope when I was discouraged. My car became my classroom of continuous education, even better than attending a University. Here I could choose from numerous lectures and learn at my own pace. In place of a once coveted Ph.D., I gained invaluable knowledge. I am nowhere near being finished with my "car education;" on any given day I have at least one set of edifying CDs on the passenger seat as learning continues.

Journaling

Writing is therapeutic and healing. Studies show that writing creatively for about fifteen minutes increases production of mood-elevating serotonin. I always liked writing, so I've been journaling about my life experiences and feelings on and off, all my life. I discovered therapeutic writing classes designed specifically to help people deal with painful memories and events by writing them down, even though I never attended any. I write rather sporadically and when all is well, I forget to write altogether. But when something troubles me greatly, I open my journal and write my heart out. I can feel release flowing out of me through the pen onto the pages, emptying the dark corners of my soul. Through ink into words—what exhilarating freedom for emotions that are stuck deep inside, seeking expression.

J. K. Rowling said: "I have to write for my own mental health" and I agree with this statement one hundred percent. These pages of mine that you now read were originally meant for self-expression and escape. I often record simple and unimportant events in my life. It helps to put my thoughts in perspective.

When I was young, I often felt lonely and isolated but didn't share my feelings and emotions with family and friends. I discovered the great healing effect of pouring my thoughts and feelings into a journal. When I was a teenager, I was afraid someone would find my journal, so I scribbled the entries and then hid it.

For many years I wrote in hardbound journals, then switched to electronic form on my phone and tablet. It was also convenient to dictate my thoughts. But something was missing. There is something special about writing words longhand in my own handwriting. Just think about it—your handwriting is unique, unlike anybody else's…

I usually take notes in church. I also used electronic note taking for a while but now I am back to "basics" with a pen and a journal with a pretty cover.

Rather than seek advice from a person, I would sometimes just need to read, think, reflect and write. As a result of such escape, I see clearly what needs to be done and whether I need to continue being still and quiet or move full speed ahead.

On occasion I pull old journals off the shelf and read them. It reminds me of events I had forgotten about and helps to keep things in perspective. I count as my mentors and coaches not only people I met in person but also authors from whose works I learned. Author and speaker Jim Rohn said: "A life worth living is a life worth recording." I think it gives a very interesting perspective on journaling. I have a habit of writing down ideas, memos, and names of books I want to read. In the age of Smart phones, I often just dictate a note or memo. Actually, this is how this book came to be—from notes, journal entries, and short memos I dictated into my phone. I put these puzzle pieces together until they seemed to fit.

Memory Box

I have a few boxes filled with sentimental and nostalgic objects I don't want to display, but I am not ready to part with. I like re-reading cards and notes I received over the years. I also like looking at old photos of friends, family and I laughing and having a great time.

There often are many things around the house that bring sweet memories. I don't want to be a packrat, so I thin out my memorabilia, leaving the most precious possessions. I keep a few things my son made when he was little. I had a huge box for years, but then together we sifted through, choosing the most special ones. As for the rest, we took pictures of many things and then let them go. We can't hold on to every single memory forever.

Then there are things we would never want to part with. I have two very special necklaces that were given to me by my father when I was young. They are precious and are worth to me more that diamonds. Even though one of them is just a pretty piece of plastic on a string. Another special item is a maternity dress my brother sewed for me a few decades ago. When I need a special emotional lift, I put it on. It's nice to wear a piece of jewelry or clothing given by a dear friend or a family member that brings good feelings and cheers me up.

Holding or wearing objects that are dear to my heart makes me calm and centered. It is one of the tools I use to distract myself from anxiety taking control. It is useful to put a few pictures and small special things in a box to know where they are and pull it out when extreme pick-me-up intervention is needed, when on occasion I feel down and miserable.

Ebenezer was a rock that the ancient Israelites erected to remind future generations of God's faithfulness. We also have a tendency to forget miracles that the Lord performed in the past when faced with life's challenges. We need to negate the shortcomings of our memory by erecting our own "ebenezers"—keepsakes to remind us of events when God has seen us through. It can literally be rocks we find where the events took place.

Vision Board

I sometimes refer to them as "wish boards"—a collage of pictures and expressions I would like to live by or to see in my future. Over the past few years I assembled a few of such boards. They are lots of fun to work on. On large pieces of cardboard, I put a bunch of pictures I liked. I let myself feel like a little girl and just wish for events and things. They included vacation destinations (a full moon over Florence, a glacier), healthy happy people, a dream house, etc. Many of them came to pass. The most interesting one was this: on one of the boards I assembled a few years back I put two pictures that incidentally had dogs in them. I never had a dog before nor was thinking about getting one. One picture was of a woman sitting in a chair in her robe and slippers, abandoning her chores (indicated by basket of laundry by her feet and disarray in the room) and reading peacefully, a small dog by her feet. Another picture was of a dog lying on its back with eyes closed in total bliss and I liked the attitude of this animal. When a few years later I was ready to replace this board with new pictures, I realized most of images of things I liked to be, do or have actually came to pass, including the dog I adopted! Guess what is her favorite pastime? To lie on her back, paws up, an epitome of total peace in all her body, just like the picture I chose for myself years back. Go figure...

Someone may think that vision boards are a part of "prosperity gospel" that is being criticized widely. After all, King Solomon did not ask for riches but for wisdom. In my opinion, we can ask for what we think we need if it is to be used for His glory. I don't *lust* after things and events I wish to happen in my life, but would *like* them to occur. In the end, it's what Lord's will for my life is, not what I want. I don't want to be self-centered. I want to keep dreaming and growing, trying to figure out what is God's will for my life, what is my ministry. I want to focus on the ultimate outcome, the purpose of this race we call life. I want to pursue that with all my heart, pleasing Him. Making a collage just helps to remind me of what tools I might use to achieve it. One of the images I currently have on my vision board is of a hamster in a maze with a phrase under it: "Never, never, never give up'. Another one is of a mouse tiptoeing in front of a sleeping cat with a quote by Eleanor Roosevelt:" Every day do at least one thing that scares you".

Working on putting together a vision board helps to me calm down and focus on positive images. Seeing pictures of audiences full of smiling people, beautiful places I would like to visit and people who represent health, energy and joy keep me encouraged and optimistic.

PART TWO

BODY INSIDE AND OUT

CHAPTER NINE

Nuts and Bolts of Healing

"The most wasted of all days is one without laughter."
E. E. Cummings

When I was experiencing fierce panic, I had a feeling that it would never end and that I might die right then and there. My husband likes to say: "This too shall pass." There is a similar phrase in the Bible: *"Commit your way to the Lord, trust also in Him, and He shall bring it to pass." (Psalm 37:5, NKJV)* I knew it must be true, however it was hard to believe. Speeding up this process of getting better faster became a quest.

Breathing

We all need to get enough oxygen to function. When I feel as if I am gasping for air, I make sure to focus on deep breathing. The key is breathing slowly and deeply into the lower abdomen and making sure to avoid shallow breathing. Sometimes I put my hand under my navel and try to breath in, focusing on that area and lifting my hand with each inhale. I pause at the top of the inhale and then slowly breathe out. I have come across various breathing techniques for relaxation—all of them designed to slow down breathing and many use the practice of counting breaths. For example, count to four on inhale, hold the breath for four counts, and then exhale on eight. It helps to slow down the breathing as well as provides distraction from troubling thoughts. Repeating this sequence ten to fifteen times provides much needed oxygen and has a calming effect.

The beauty of deep breathing technique is that it could be done anytime, anywhere. Even when I was in my car or so low physically and emotionally that I couldn't move, it was still available.

Changing Physiology

It is scientifically proven that mental conditions depend on our biochemistry. It is also established that by changing our physiology, we can change our biochemistry. By specifically using a few different methods, I can bring immediate changes to my body and help improve or alter my frame of mind, allowing me to escape from an "attack." Changing posture, facial expression and breathing is all part of this strategy. As soon as I learned these simple techniques, I knew I could rapidly ease the feelings of anxiety. At first I couldn't force my body to do too much and so I retreated and turned to medication to give me a boost. As I practiced these techniques more and more, they became second nature. I began using them to calm my body and mind automatically. If I get anxious for any reason, I straighten up, put a smile on my face and begin breathing deeply and fully. Regaining the sense of control of my body helped to release the paralyzing grip of fear during an "episode."

Body of a Warrior, Not a Worrier

Changing my posture to an upright position, widening my shoulders and breathing deeply can often change my mood in a matter of minutes. There is a passage in the Bible that refers to us standing in God's grace: *"Through Him we have also obtained access by faith into this grace in which we stand, and we rejoice in hope of the glory of God." (Romans 5:2, ESV).* I like envisioning myself standing in the grace of God, surrounded by his love, stretching hands upward, rejoicing.

Research at major universities has shown the connection between posture and the body's neuro-endocrine response. One study showed that people who stood straight and had their hands locked behind their heads for two minutes experienced their cortisol level drop by about 25 percent. In another study, clinically depressed people were asked to stand straight in front of a mirror and grin from ear to ear for about twenty minutes during each session. At the end of the study (which took a few weeks), some of the participants no longer required their medication! A combination of posture change and facial expression can significantly affect the body's response to stress or depression.

Laughter is a Serious Matter

Why do so many videos of laughing babies or baby animals playing go viral? Do we crave the relief and joy such videos evoke in us? We need all the smiles and giggles we can get from watching them, and they make us feel good. By the way, babies don't have to hear jokes to laugh, they just do. We need to release our inner child and smile and laugh more readily. Unfortunately, in our busy lives, many of us frown more often than laugh.

Before I ever heard the statement that happiness is a choice, I intuitively tried to live it. When I was working at the International School in Kiev, some of my colleagues commented on me smiling all the time. My facial expression was quite different from that of the majority of people they encountered in the city. I got into the habit of putting a smile on my face as I was approaching the building where I worked. Let me tell you, it was not an easy task: after waiting in freezing wind and snow for a bus and once aboard, being squished and pushed, so I was not a happy camper after my hour-long commute. I made it a conscious effort to smile.

I was raised in a culture where smiling or laughing for no reason was perceived as a sign of a shallow person. But I have noticed that smiling made me feel better, so I got into the habit of smiling regularly. It became a part of a survival mechanism and it worked miracles.

The first time I put a fake grin on my face and held it for a few minutes, I was surprised by the results. Encouraged by what I experienced, I became determined to smile more, even when I didn't feel like it. It took time, because it had to become second nature, a new habit. There are somewhat different opinions on how long it takes a person to develop a new habit, but research shows that it takes between one and two and a half months. I think it depends on the person and the task at hand, but with enough determination, it is possible to establish new, healthy habits relatively fast.

Smiling is beneficial, but laughing out loud changes a person's biochemistry much faster. I compare it to walking and jogging. Movement in both is good, but breaking a sweat is better for increasing the flow of oxygen and releasing endorphins. Five minutes of belly laughing is a great emotional workout as well as a physical workout. When we laugh really hard, we get an increase of oxygen flow to the brain and the release of beneficial chemicals.

When I catch myself frowning, I stretch my lips into a smile, even if nothing is funny. I am more likely to laugh out loud when I am alone in my car, where no one can see or hear me. I don't want to scare people by appearing crazy! It was hard at first, so I listened to comedy on the radio and made myself grin even if I didn't think the jokes were particularly funny. Let me remind you, healing took a lot of effort. I had to practice, and at times even forced myself into action. Now, laughing on cue is yet another quick fix when I need relief from stress.

A woman described in Proverbs 31 "laughs at the time to come" Prov.31:25 (ESV). I want to be able to do just that! Another translation, NKJV, uses the word "rejoices" instead of "laughs." I like both versions. This slight difference just reminds me why I like switching between different translations when I do my Bible studies. I refer to various English versions, on occasion switching to translations in Ukrainian and Russian. How I wish I could read Greek and Hebrew!

Move It!

During a workout, the body produces endorphins as well as serotonin, both of which help to switch off anxiety. Regular exercise increases blood flow, lowers blood pressure, acidity and cholesterol levels.

It is much easier to move when you have energy, but what do you do when you have to gather all your energy to just cross the room? There were times when I did not want to even think about working out! At first, circling a dining room or a coffee table while talking on the phone was counted as an exercise. The next variation was to force myself off the couch and onto the floor. Some of the moves resembled a bug on its back—barely moving its limbs. Though I was an exercise junkie in the past, vigorous movement was unappealing to me in this condition. I would just stretch on the floor or do light Pilates exercises. The term "yoga" relates to spiritual practice as much as movement, but if you sign up for a yoga class at your local gym, most likely you would only learn to breathe for optimal oxygen intake, to pay specific attention to various areas in your body, release tension, as well as stretching and asymmetric poses, using various muscles in your body. Deep breathing with attention to strengthening my body in a stretch was incredibly beneficial. It increased blood flow and helped to switch the focus from current circumstances to movement in the current moment. This type of exercise, as well as other relaxation techniques, helped soothe exhausted adrenal glands.

There were days when I had eight to ten physically and mentally excruciating anxiety attacks. Alleviation came when I peeled myself off the couch, got on a mat and focused on breathing and moving slowly. It was an absolute Godsend! Even a tiny break from the cloud of despair was a huge relief. Now when I do these slow stretches on the beach, or elsewhere in nature, I marvel at God's creation and the miracle of my own body: lungs, heart, limbs and all other parts working together in unison. It truly is a gift from above to be there, breathing.

I have CDs with various exercises and I use them often, as well as workout routines I recorded on TV or stream from the Internet. It suits me well, as I like variety and was able to find the workout customized to the way I was feeling at the moment. During the worst times, workouts helped me tremendously; and at times it was the only port in the storm. I think if a person is willing to exercise and has their doctor's approval, he or she may find the type of exercise their body can tolerate and routines that fit each lifestyle. It is never too late to start. I remember watching programs where ladies in their nineties went to the gym and lifted weights! I want to do that when I "grow up". Even the simplest moves increase blood circulation. Walking, stretching, dancing, simple workout moves—I try to incorporate them all, depending on how I feel or how much time I have.

I always liked taking scenic walks. The problem was that depression immobilized my body; so it was a monumental task to drag myself off the couch and out of the house. On occasion, my friends became my walking companions. Thankfully, I got a dog and now, rain or shine, I take her for a walk, slowly waking up as I lag behind my happily trotting pooch. Recently I rediscovered swimming, which became a great outlet for my inner mermaid. It's one of my favorite activities and a great way to elevate my mood.

Healing Waters

Anything that has to do with touching warm water has a calming effect on me, including long showers, taking a bath or swimming. For me, being submerged in warm water evokes peace and unity with nature, as well as the safety of the womb. Maybe there is a connection with our body and the planet both consisting of seventy percent water.

When I was growing up, we had a nice-sized tub and I loved splashing in it. Some of my favorite childhood memories include visiting either one of my grandmothers and taking baths at their houses. Grandmas usually pamper generously, and mine were no exception! In my paternal grandmother's flat, an instant water heater unit was hung on the wall in the bathroom. I can still hear the hissing of water going through the coiled brass pipes over gas burners. I loved to watch the flames, especially during winter, when I got in the tub of very warm water after playing in the snow for hours. It was as close to heaven as I knew, especially because after my bath, I would go to grandma's bedroom and dive onto a freshly fluffed, thick down blanket, and it would surround me as a soft white cloud. Now I can evoke the experience by taking a bath or even a nice hot shower, then climb in bed and close my eyes. I am instantly transformed from an adult to a little happy girl visiting her grandma—even if for a fleeting moment…

Actually, you don't need to take a bath or a shower to elevate your mood. Researchers in Germany found that even washing your face with warm soapy water increases the brain's production of calming alpha waves and may provide psychological relief. Another study conducted showed that people who were floating in water for up to an hour indicated decrease in production of cortisol, adrenaline and feel-good endorphins.

There is one more thing I want to share with you. I have not met too many people who like to wash dishes by hand, but since childhood it's been one of my favorite things to do—washing plates and cups in warm soapy water. It always soothed me to hear running water, to sense the warmth running from my fingers through my whole body. Using a nice smelling soap adds to this positive experience.

Stress-Reducing Scents

The pleasant aroma of some plants have been used for relaxing baths and massages or burned as incense for centuries. Now scientific research proves the benefit of essential oils. It was observed that some scents have a soothing effect. Essential oils like frankincense, rose, lavender, rosemary, patchouli, neroli, lemon, sweet orange, vanilla or chamomile have relaxing properties and can help to lift moods, alleviate depression and relieve anxiety. Inhaling their pleasant aromas activate the parasympathetic nervous system, increase alpha brain waves and decrease cortisol levels therefore lowering levels of stress. Nowadays various essential oils are widely available, especially at health food stores and online. When shopping for these oils, I look for 100% organic ones, as they don't have dangerous chemical additives.

My top favorites are lavender and rose oils. I like to carry a little spray bottle filled with a mix of distilled water and rose oil. Spraying it over my face and neck in hot summer months is especially refreshing. I also use it to mist my sheets before going to bed. I made a small sachet of lavender blossoms to keep by my bed and I refresh it now and then with a few drops of lavender oil. This scent helps to promote deep restorative sleep.

Sometimes I sniff my favorite essential oils from a bottle or put a few drops on my hands. They may also be added to a bath for a spa-like experience. Recently I bought a diffuser that fills the room with fine fragrant mist and also works as a humidifier.

Catering to the Senses

Smelling pleasant aromas suppresses the production of cortisol and adrenalin, lifting the mood as a result. When I pass by a lavender plant while walking, I often pick a sprig, rub it between my fingers to release the oils and smell it. I also smell roses wherever I see them. In my neighborhood, I got to a point where I recognize plants with the most fragrant blooms and make sure to stop and smell them.

I used to have asthma and allergies, so in the past smelling flowers, perfume or perfumed lotions was not an option. After eliminating refined carbohydrates and dairy products from my diet for prolonged periods of time, going for acupuncture as well as taking supplements, I got rid of these problems and I can wear perfume and smell the flowers again. I also stop and look at beautiful scenery, taking it all in. Looking at beautiful flowers or scenery stimulates the brain's production of stress-decreasing alpha waves.

Light and color can be used to affect our mood and health. I did not study chromotherapy in depth, but noticed that when I look at certain lighter colors I feel better. Even the colors of clothes I wear can affect my mood, so I try to choose carefully. Choosing the right color to paint walls in my house is important too, as the colors I surround myself on a regular basis are essential for well-being. I have a tendency to avoid walking into the rooms that are painted dark.

I once came across colored glasses to be used for color therapy. It reminded me that once I had pink-tinted sunglasses and they actually helped with my mood! Recently various coloring books for adults appeared at numerous stores. I realized I do not like the ones that already have too much black ink outlining the pictures; I prefer the ones with barely visible lines, the ones I can color in with vibrant, bright colors. Even the apps for therapeutic coloring are available. Coloring incorporates both sight and touch. Both can be used in fighting anxiety. I mentioned earlier that the first therapist I visited suggested bringing a soft toy or a small blanket to our therapy sessions. The idea was to create a sense of security as I touch soft fabric.

Massage

Enjoyable touch is one of the benefits of therapeutic massage. Getting a massage is one of my top favorite things to relax. I completely melt on the table when a therapist is working my muscles. It is positively great for general relaxation as it promotes production of serotonin. I am still learning to be completely in the moment, especially on a massage table, and just dwell in this blessing, enjoying it to the fullest. No need to tell my mind to relax, or not to wander to my to-do list or the last unpleasant conversation I had with so-and-so.

Even when I could not splurge on such indulgence or did not have time to go for a treatment, I used self-massage with rollers, especially on my back and feet. I also used nice smelling lotion to massage hands and arms, which is very relaxing. Massage of the scalp I can do myself, either by using a brush or by gently rubbing the top of my head with my fingers.

Reflexology

Even before I became familiar with acupressure I noticed how such self-massages or a quick shoulder rub improved my mood and overall state. It made me feel better instantly. I later learned a few specific acupressure points, which when pressed can trigger positive emotional response and relieve symptoms of anxiety. A few are located on the back of the neck and shoulders. There are specific points located on the inside of wrists, inside elbows and on the head, including the ones along the hairline and between the eyebrows. Gentle self-massage of these areas help me to release tension. Pressing a few points on my collarbone and breastbone helps to relieve nervousness as well.

Emotional Freedom Technique

Emotional Freedom Technique is also known as EFT or tapping. I understand it is similar to reflexology and massage. Studies have shown that EFT reduces the cortisol level in the body up to 25%, which is pretty significant. There are videos available on YouTube with instruction. I watched them numerous times to memorize the sequence. Now that I know it, I can do them anywhere, even on the beach.

Acupuncture

I definitely prefer a good massage to being poked with needles. The majority of us strongly dislike any sort of needles being inserted in our body.

I heard of acupuncture for years without seriously considering it. The idea of multiple needles being stuck in my body for a prolonged time did not sound the least bit appealing. I always opted for a massage rather than acupuncture until I discovered its many benefits. Testimonies of patients who praised it for the relief it provided opened me towards it, but I was still indecisive. Then I visited my father's cousin in New York, who became an acupuncturist after moving to this country. Back in Russia, he was a prominent cardiologist but transferring his diploma and skills to his new homeland was too complicated. He still wanted to help people, so he chose this route. In his acupuncture practice he had great results with anxiety and allergies in his patients, two conditions I suffered from. I was staying in New York for only a few days, so he could not work on me, but was willing to explain how it works. Insertion of hair-thin needles in specific spots helps to improve the body's inner balancing by affecting the energy flow. Acupuncture increases the body's ability to heal itself as well as production of endorphins and serotonin. I was still skeptical until I tried this type of treatment myself and experienced great results.

Desperation called for drastic measures. Upon return to California, I looked up a few referrals and found a great Korean doctor who treated me on and off for various conditions for a few years. Usually results were positive after the first visit, but would wear off after some time. It took a few weeks to receive the full benefit and feel significant improvement. It has to be repeated from time to time but it did provide relief without heavy drugs, which is a big plus for me. Eventually I found that acupuncture is a powerful therapy that is beneficial in treating a great number of medical conditions by restoring balance in the patient's body. The latest sessions even allowed me to resume drinking coffee without adverse effect, which was a welcome side effect.

Occasionally doctors of Asian medicine prescribed and dispensed herbs, mostly in the form of an instant tea. By no means were they pleasant-tasting drinks! But those concoctions effectively kept anxiety at bay. They also helped to improve and eliminate other issues like allergies and occasional colds, as well as various pains and aches. The major noticeable effect of taking such herbs was a general relaxed state.

Unfortunately, I did not discover the benefits of Asian medicine and acupuncture early enough. I had to turn to medication and try other natural remedies first.

Progressive Muscle Relaxation

This technique is based on tensing and releasing different muscle groups for short periods of time in combination with deep abdominal breathing. Sitting in a chair, I slowly breathe in and out, making sure to use abdominal breathing. After that I would begin to tighten and relax facial muscles, hands, arms, shoulders, back, stomach, thighs, legs and feet. I do it for each muscle group separately for five seconds on inhale, then relax as I slowly exhale. Focusing on breathing and on different parts of the body changes the flow of thoughts. It reduces cortisol levels and delivers oxygen to the cells. Some studies show that it reduces blood pressure. It has an overall calming effect.

Lack of Sleep

Getting enough sleep is crucial for our wellbeing and sleep deprivation is a serious health issue. Most adults need about eight hours of sleep for optimal health. Lack of sleep is associated not only with the body's cognitive functions, but also moodiness, weight gain and lack of productivity are just a few results of sleep deprivation. It can affect our emotions and self- control. It is not a luxury but a necessity for well-being and disease prevention. Catching up on much-needed sleep a few days a week significantly reduces the production of cortisol by our bodies, which reduces the stress levels.

Exposure to sun is crucial in the production of melatonin, the hormone that affects sleep cycles. We also need exposure to sun to synthesize vitamin D through the skin, which helps regulate serotonin levels in the brain. Allowing sunshine on the skin for about ten minutes daily without sunscreen is what I aim for. Evening walks can improve sleep quality as experiencing a sunset stimulates the production of melatonin. When I was working long hours in artificially lit rooms, I was not getting enough exposure to natural sunlight. It affected my overall mood as well as immune system. "Winter blues" are all too familiar to me. When I was living in a cold climate with significantly shorter days, I was not getting sufficient exposure to sunlight, which did lower my mood and cause disruption in sleep.

A drop in progesterone, which acts as a sedative, may cause insomnia as well. This hormone is produced by adrenal glands, which also produce adrenaline. When adrenals are exhausted, it wreaks havoc on hormonal balance.

Drinking caffeinated drinks in the afternoon can disrupt the sleep cycle in many. For me, any drink that contains even small amounts of caffeine became a no-no after noon if I didn't want to toss and turn late into the night. Dark chocolate has a similar effect.

Taking some supplement or medication such as vitamin B or SSRI medications late in the day may also affect sleep.

I avoid going to bed shortly after a heavy meal; also, sleeping in a cooler room induces the overall quality of sleep.

Taking valerian root supplement can induce better sleep through relaxation. It usually takes over a month of taking valerian root three times a day to see significant improvement.

During many a sleepless night, I used to toss and turn, dwelling on a problem. Now I turn all life challenges over to God. I begin to pray or recite Bible verses, or meditate on the Fruit of the Spirit (love, joy, peace, patience, kindness, goodness, gentleness and self-control). Eventually I will fall asleep in peace.

Excessive Tiredness

I know that working out regularly, especially doing cardiovascular exercises that cause rapid blood circulation, need to be performed three times a week or so. Done regularly, it helps my body to restore its energy levels. With regular exercise and healthy eating, I was able to stay on track for long periods of time, enjoying the benefits of increased energy, endurance, concentration. Then "life happens," as they say. I will get distracted with stress-causing events at work or at home. Somehow under emotional pressure, the healthy lifestyle often flies out the window. When I try to survive, I don't focus on health as much—big mistake. It spirals downward from there… When I don't exercise, my body gradually becomes sluggish and it is very hard to get back on track. When I was fighting severe anxiety and depression spells, I didn't feel like moving at all. Forget hopping up and down and jogging—that basically became an unachievable quest. I felt like a deflated balloon with all the energy drained out of me, leaving an empty shell.

Even when I did work out, I needed to pay attention to what time of the day I felt more energetic. Working out in the afternoon often gave me an energy boost instead of draining it.

Many of us are tired because we do too much. There are also many underlying biochemical causes of chronic fatigue that need to be properly addressed. We don't need to suffer if the cure to chronic low energy is obtainable. Fatigue may be connected to lack of certain nutrients and chemicals in the body: iron, for example. Overconsumption of carbohydrates (especially refined carbohydrates like sugar, baked goods and pasta) also leads to tiredness. Hormonal fluctuations, especially during perimenopause and menopause, can cause fatigue and exhaustion. Disrupted thyroid function can cause excess tiredness as well.

A naturopathic doctor helped me to address this issue on a few different occasions. After taking blood tests, she recommended a correct hormonal diet and supplements. Each time I felt much better within days.

CHAPTER TEN

Medications and Natural Remedies

*"Their fruit will be for food,
and their leaves for medicine."*
Ezekiel 47:12, NKJV

I wished many times there was a magic pill I could take to chase away anxiety and depression forever, never to haunt me. Yes, there are substances that can work instantly to temporarily take my problems away. Medications from the benzodiazepines group could numb my senses in a matter of minutes. A glass of wine can give me an illusion of escape. But what about side effects? These remedies are potentially addictive. I was always acutely aware of anything that may cause addiction and avoided it as much as I could. Even when I was prescribed painkillers after a few surgeries that I had, I used the bare minimum for fear of getting addicted. Tranquilizers may calm acute anxiety, but I did not want to rely on them long-term.

A group of medications called SSRI (Selective Serotonin Reuptake Inhibitors) are often prescribed to patients suffering from anxiety and depression as a long-term solution. It takes time for such medications to accumulate in a patient's body. Correcting the chemical imbalance in the brain takes some time. It took about two weeks for me to feel the full effect of an SSRI medication I was prescribed. It did take the edge off my anxiety, but I felt odd, as if sitting in a jar of cotton balls. My feelings were so cushioned, they were almost non-existent. I welcomed the relief from acute anxiety, but didn't like the lack of other emotions. More than ever, I was committed to finding other solutions and therapies. I was on a path to healing, determined to eventually lead a happy, anxiety-free and, if I could, medication-free life. I didn't want to endure side effects for long but rather, to help my body produce its own serotonin as well as mood-boosting endorphins.

I was positive these natural methods and therapies were out there for me to find. Once I realized I could improve my situation by educating myself, I was filled with hope. Finally, I saw light at the end of the tunnel I was stuck in and was ready to peruse everything available for my healing.

Research

I have to admit I didn't use the Internet much in my research. There are a couple of reasons. First, I have a tendency to "get lost" in virtual reality and barely resurface for air. There were times when I was highly addicted to surfing the net and checking into social media for hours at a time. That had to change, so I limited my time on-line only to necessary e-mail checking a few times a week. With internet research, I often had trouble staying focused on only the question at hand and hours later would find myself reading some totally unrelated article. I also can't trust everything I read on-line and it takes too much extra time to verify information. For me, books and magazines were much easier to manage and trust.

To sum up, I aimed to be a well-educated patient. I became informed on diet and supplements that affect the mind-body connection. I observed my own body's reaction to various stressors and foods.

Dopamine and Serotonin

A chemical imbalance in a person's body can wreak havoc on his emotions. There are various ways to restore this balance. Correctly prescribed medication as well as supplements, herbs, diet and exercise prove to be beneficial. There are also numerous coping mechanisms that can stabilize the release of dopamine, serotonin and endorphins to make us feel significantly better in shorter periods of time. With time, I assembled quite a list of potential stress-reducing remedies. I sought a way to wellness with minimal side effects. I was so weary of pain that I often didn't apply only one method to wait and see if it worked. I used various relaxation techniques and remedies simultaneously. Looking back, I think I should have waited to see what worked best, but I was desperate. Through trial and error, I sifted through various remedies to reduce overall stress and anxiety symptoms and found what works best for me. It took me a long time to pinpoint the best ways to stop anxiety from taking control over my body and mind and become paralyzing. I could choose from deep breathing, laughing or a call to a girlfriend for a fun chat. Then there are stress-reducing techniques such as acupuncture, diet adjustments, and regular workouts, to name a few. The mind-body connection never ceased to fascinate me. We truly are wonderfully made!

Preventative Medicine and Conventional Medicine

These two should work side by side. I was fortunate to have a family practitioner that was knowledgeable not only in conventional therapies but also in preventative and alternative medicine. I saw this doctor on a regular basis for over a year. She was the one who prescribed my SSRI and Benzodiazepine medications and gave me so much good advice. She gave great recommendations, adjusting medication and supplements, and suggested various non-traditional methods of medicine, mainly for relaxation purposes. But she didn't specialize in psychology, naturopathy or acupuncture, so my quest continued. Only later did I discover herbs and supplements that worked even better for me than conventional medication.

Drugs: Pros and Cons

For months I refused to take any SSRI drugs. I refused to accept that my condition was merely a deficiency of Prozac or some other medication. Eventually, I succumbed but it took some convincing from my doctor to try one. I was not aware then of the majority of other therapies. In my case, taking medication worked, and I stayed on it for nine months, being closely monitored by a doctor. It made a big difference in my life. If you know how depression feels, let me tell you, it is as if my world was like the beginning of "The Wizard of Oz" movie, and then, after a couple of weeks of taking ten milligrams of meds a day, it slowly turned into a Technicolor rainbow—colors and feelings I missed for months. I experienced joy again.

The SSRI medication I was prescribed didn't work right away. It had to build up in my system gradually, which took about two weeks. Then the heaviness of anxiety slowly lifted. I experienced a slight mental fog, but still better than a sense of hopelessness and overwhelming fear I experienced for far too long. I thought I could stay on this medication for a while, but only a definite period of time seemed agreeable to me.

Side Effects

There are numerous other possible side effects listed for anti-anxiety medications, including nausea, stomachache, and even suicidal thoughts. Another side effect that is not often talked about is a loss of libido. While singles that practice abstinence may welcome it, for married people it may cause extra discord of relationships already affected by a mood disorder.

Mood-altering medications and supplements made me drowsy. I also experienced extreme vivid dreaming. Not that I had too many nightmares, but in the morning I could recall more dreams than usual and it was hard to get up in the morning. I was tired, did not feel well-rested and energetic and could not wait for the time when I did not need to take anything.

Many people I talked to have been taking mood-altering medications for years. For me, the main side effect, even with a small dose, was losing my senses overall. I felt as if I was slowly moving through a light cloud, which was uncomfortable and I knew I couldn't tolerate that for long.

It was crucial to ask questions about all drugs prescribed and my experiences with them, including contraindications. But taking myself off medication without a doctor's supervision could have made matters much worse. Unlike many other drugs, SSRI accumulate in the body over time, and abruptly quitting them may wreak total havoc on the system, so the patient needs to wean from them slowly. Nowadays there is a wide array of medication available to treat mental conditions, and an experienced doctor will find the correct one and adjust the dosage according to the patient's needs and reaction.

Trial and Error of Medication: Adjustment

Doctors run tests, ask questions, observe patient's behavior, then write a prescription. I was curious to know which ones of the most popular I'll get: Zoloft, Xanax, Lexapro or the grandpa of them all: Prozac. My doctor's choice was Lexapro. As far as I know, there are no definitive tests to pinpoint the exact medication and dose that a patient needs. A doctor will use his expertise and guidelines, prescribe a particular medication, then observe how it works and make adjustments as necessary. Some conditions may require a cocktail of meds, but in my case, I did well with what I tried first, although mild side effects convinced me to get off it as soon as my doctor approved. When my doctor thought I was ready to get off my medication, she gradually decreased my dosage until I was free to live without it. I still had a prescription for Lorazepam, which works very fast, but only to be used on occasion of acute anxiety.

I was eager to emerge from the thin layer of brain fog into a bright light. At first my senses were not as sharp as they used to be before the illness and I still experienced ups and downs, but I was not afraid. I wanted to live to the fullest without being numbed. I was longing to regain my life and to learn to correct occasional chemical imbalances in the most natural way possible. I even sought out controversial treatments.

Medical Marijuana

For centuries opium, marijuana and other plant-based concoctions were used to treat a wide range of maladies. In the past, even opium and cocaine were prescribed as remedies for various diseases. After it was discovered how addictive these substances are and how damaging they can be to one's health, they became outlawed. Nowadays there is a lot of disagreement about the use of medical marijuana and its healing properties. At the risk of controversy, a little explanation may cause opponents to change their minds. Currently, there is more research being conducted by the FDA on the healing properties of cannabis (medical marijuana). This herb is not just being used as a "sinful potion," even though many know it as an illegal drug solely used to get high or feed an addiction. Have you not also heard of people becoming addicted to pharmaceutical painkillers? Addiction can sprout from various sources. Some people get addicted easier than others, for whatever reason, and in such cases psychological help is necessary.

In some states, medical marijuana is legal and has been used successfully to treat patients with cancer, chronic pain, Post Traumatic Stress Disorder and anxiety. Medical marijuana may help patients get rid of pain that otherwise can only be helped by strong medications with damaging side effects.

I thought for a person with anxiety there may be relief from taking certain herbs and this particular one as well. I was willing to give it a try, obtained a prescription and found out that for me it didn't work the way I was hoping. I expected to become pleasantly relaxed, but I experienced brain-fog that I disliked, and my anxiety didn't disappear, though somewhat decreased. With marijuana, it is hard to control the intake of cannabis, whether it is smoked or consumed in treats; it is also hard to predict how it will affect a person. There are a few varieties that supposedly affect patients differently. After a few tries, I gave up on this remedy and moved on to other ones, as it did not help. It is possible that I was so afraid to get addicted that my body did not accept it as a potential remedy. Thus, the search to finding effective natural remedies continued after this detour.

Herbal Supplements

There are various herbs with calming, relaxing and tranquilizing properties: Passionflower, Gensing, Kava, Gotu Kola, Ashwagandha, Valerian root.

Ashwagandha balances cortisol and adds energy but is gentle and doesn't over-stimulate the body. It might help to reduce inflammation. My naturopathic doctor recommended it and I found it helpful.

Passionflower tea is known to promote relaxation and to have anti-insomnia properties.

When I was living in Europe, St.John's Wort was often used to treat depression and anxiety. This herb aids in production of norepinephrine, a neurotransmitter that helps to improve mood.

Valerian root was another European go-to herb for reducing mild stress and inducing relaxation. It was often used before going to bed to aid in restful sleep. I tried to drink it as tea, by itself and in combination with chamomile and other herbs, but didn't really like the taste or smell. Supplements in a capsule form were a little better, but I was still able to taste it—yuck! Unfortunately, many stress-reducing teas I found at health food stores had too much of this herb to make it a pleasant drink for me; maybe that is why I opted for a glass of wine! There were other relaxation-promoting caffeine-free teas with a much more pleasant taste, some available at regular grocery stores.

I came across studies that suggested eight weeks of three daily doses of Valerian root for significant improvement in stress and anxiety symptoms. Surprisingly to me, results of other studies showed that this herb also acts as a mild depressant and should not be used for prolonged periods of time... It also suggested that some people may become too drowsy in the morning and that should not be used in combination with alcohol as both may trigger depression. It can get confusing so, as with all medications and supplements, I sought my doctor's approval before using anything. She warned me, for example, that taking St.John's Wort increases sun sensitivity. I was told that herbs should not be taken with prescription antidepressants. There are very few studies conducted on combining herbs and conventional western drugs, so I didn't supplement with herbs when I was on SSRI medication. Not many conventional doctors are trained in natural medicine but they can advise on taking mineral supplements and vitamins when needed. Later I learned about many mood-enhancing supplements and herbs as well as alternative remedies.

Some herbs and supplements are potentially harmful, especially in certain combinations with each other or medication. To avoid mistakes, I didn't hesitate to ask questions, especially in conversations with a naturopathic doctor.

Supplements

When I am anxious, my body experiences chemical imbalance, so it is important to nurture my precious self with delicious healthy foods. It also helps to add proper supplements as even organically grown, pasture-raised, antibiotic and pesticide-free foods can be lacking in vital nutrients. In addition, some microelements are hard to obtain from common foods, and not many of us eat Brazil nuts or beef liver, as nutritious as they are. I didn't know exactly what my body was lacking, so my doctor ran blood tests to figure it out. I actually need to have these blood tests done about once a year to see what is going on and if I need supplementation. I prefer these tests to be reviewed by a doctor trained in naturopathy.

When I eat right and exercise, I am likely to be healthy overall, not as susceptible to anxiety, allergies, insomnia, digestive problems or even colds and flu. By eating right, I mean a strict diet of organic produce, pasture-raised, grass-fed meat, poultry and dairy, no refined carbohydrates whatsoever, limited caffeinated drinks like coffee and tea, and no alcohol. Many of my friends asked the inevitable question: "Why live if you remove all pleasure in life?" When you are facing a serious illness or tremendous pain, you will do *anything* to reverse it. Moreover, if you eat a clean healthy diet for a while, you become used to it and begin enjoying the taste of simple foods, like unaltered fruit and vegetables. After a week or two of eliminating the intake of refined carbohydrates (breads, pastries, sweets) my body stopped craving such foods. I read that it is often the yeast overgrowth in our bodies that cause cravings of sweets. I really don't want to feed the yeast when I eat muffins or cupcakes. I need to feed myself for energy and well-being. Unfortunately, temptations are everywhere and I do waver from strictly clean eating for periods of time.

I listened to a book on CD called "The Great Physician's Rx for Health and Wellness" by Jordan Rubin. He gives great advice on diet, healthy lifestyle and natural (non-synthetic only) supplements. An increased number of studies show how nutrition affects our mood and susceptibility to anxiety. Most of us eat a diet poor in nutrients. Ideally, we should get all necessary vitamins, minerals, proteins and other substances from our food, but for many of us this is lacking, so we need to add nutrients by way of supplements.

Here is a quick overview of supplements I found beneficial on the road to mental wellbeing:

Omega-3 and vitamin D help regulate serotonin levels in the brain. Serotonin production drops during winter months due to lack of sunlight exposure when our bodies produce decreased amounts of vitamin D. Even in summer months, our bodies don't usually produce adequate amounts of vitamin D as we use sunblocks and other forms of protection from the sun. Recently I read in various sources that we need about ten to fifteen minutes of direct sun exposure daily. Doctors, after running a blood test, may detect deficiency of this vitamin and recommend a supplement.

Iron deficiency, low levels of calcium, magnesium, zinc and other essential elements can also lead to anxiety and depression. I am prone to anemia and need to check my ferritin levels regularly. When I work out vigorously, sweat and drink lots of water, I am eliminating toxins (a plus) as well as microelements (a minus) and need to get them back in my system. This is why electrolyte-enriched water is popular among health-conscious athletes. Magnesium deficiency is a probable culprit for increased anxiety symptoms.

In my research, I found that low levels of iron could cause low serotonin levels as well as low energy and fatigue. There are different forms of iron, including liquid, and I learned that taking it with vitamin C and B-12 increases absorption.

Low levels of vitamin B6 may cause hyperventilation and anxiety-like symptoms. Studies show that Niacin (vitamin B-3) aids in relaxation and reduction of anxiety and depression. Research is ongoing to link deficiency of other B vitamins (like B1, B2 and B12) to stress and anxiety.

Stress triggers the production of hormones that exhausts the adrenals, which in turn worsens the problem of anxiety. Adrenal glands also produce progesterone. When adrenals are exhausted, we hit estrogen overload, which also happens with hormonal fluctuations during perimenopause. Vitamin B6 helps the liver to better metabolize excess estrogen.

It is important to have comprehensive blood tests to detect nutrient deficiencies or hormonal imbalances. It is interesting that doctors may use different guidelines. For example, when I had my ferritin levels checked, one doctor's chart showed that I was anemic and required supplementation with iron while another doctor's guideline suggested I was not deficient per se but only borderline and eating iron-rich foods was recommended. Checking hormone levels can be tricky, as they fluctuate, especially with PMS and even more so during perimenopause and menopause. But it can be done and possible imbalances could be addressed.

5-HTP (5-Hydroxythriptophan) is an amino acid that the body converts to serotonin. Adequate amounts of serotonin in the brain regulates mood, affects sleep and sensitivity to pain as well as controls appetite. I can get this amino acid with food, but it usually is not enough. Do you remember getting sleepy after a large meal that included turkey and a lot of carbohydrates like mashed potatoes, stuffing and your favorite pie? Turkey is a good source, but I usually don't eat too much. Also, the body's production of serotonin declines with age. I need to find ways to get adequate amounts of amino acids that serve as building blocks for serotonin production. Studies show that supplementing with 5-HTP is comparable to treatments with SSRI medications and can increase serotonin production faster than prescription medication. 5-HTP helps the body to produce its own serotonin, while SSRI medication helps existing serotonin to work longer. 5-HTP can be found in supplements that contain Griffonia seed extract.

As I mentioned, I had to ask my doctor to check my blood for possible vitamin and nutrient deficiencies and only then ask for advice on correct supplementation. Taking too many vitamins, supplements or herbs may have dangerous side effects if not monitored properly. I had to educate myself but also ask my physician and a naturopathic doctor. I am an advocate for self-education but definitely not for self-medicating.

CHAPTER ELEVEN

Food and Mood

"Let food be thy medicine,
thy medicine shall be thy food."
Hippocrates

Intestines and Brain Connection or Gut and Emotions

For a few years I had severe stomach pains on a daily basis. Every morning I would wake up, waiting for pain to show up and, sure enough, it did. It was the same with anxiety a few years back: on a beautiful morning I would open my eyes, feeling wonderful, and then remember that it is too good to be true, that I am supposed to have anxiety.

At first I did not make the distinct connection between the two: stomach pain and anxiety. Many types of pain are connected to our emotions. Stress can find its release through aches, pains or insomnia. But when we often blame a sleepless night on stress we experience, it is not as clear as with pain. After all, there can be numerous other causes. When my gastroenterologist told me during my first visit there was a 95% chance that my stomach problems were a reaction to stress, I was skeptical, as this stomach pain was so real. I did what I thought was necessary: went to several doctors, endured invasive and not so invasive tests. I just kept searching for medical reasons and cure. I know now that I was so focused on my pain that it caused more pain. I was certain something was seriously wrong with me.

What is the distinction between concern about health and obsession over health? Maybe if I was still seeing a psychologist, it would have helped to find the underlying anxiety, take stress-relieving supplements or even return to antidepressants for a while, my stomach pain would have been resolved—who knows. I was so used to bouts of panic and so familiar with old symptoms, I didn't realize that stress could manifest in other parts of my body. I also didn't think I was under too much stress, just regular life stuff. Hey, I was a problem solver in life, so that without serious challenges, I unwittingly invented them. May be I was even subconsciously creating health problems.

I was blind to the fact that stress can wreak havoc in my digestive system, although I recall getting stomach cramps quite often before important exams. These always quickly disappeared afterwards. So when I began having digestive issues without experiencing usual feelings of stress and anxiety, I didn't put two and two together.

Only after nearly two years of going from doctor to doctor to doctor and from test to test to even more invasive test and exhausting all options of possible disease did my symptoms disappear overnight. As soon as I was assured that everything was normal and there were no more new medical tests to endure, I finally felt well. The influence of suggestion in our mind is a powerful thing! I thought something was wrong, I was stressed over it and my body reacted accordingly.

One of the reasons for my concern was that I knew stress can cause disease. I was a victim of acute anxiety for quite a long time and was wondering how it might have affected my overall health. I was fearful. As a lesson learned I now try to practice happiness as much as I can and focus on gratitude for everything in my life. I have a more positive outlook in life and daily count my blessings.

All I learned about the connection between gut and emotions I can now share with you.

Caffeine

Some people's bodies metabolize caffeine slowly and it can take up to twelve hours for the liver to break down caffeine. I happen to be one of them. Caffeine makes me more susceptible to heart palpitations and anxiety, as it increases levels of norepinephrine—a neurotransmitter responsible for alertness and decreased levels of vitamin B1. Thankfully, slow abdominal breathing, calming down and meditation can restore our bodies back to normal rather fast.

I realized early on that I am sensitive to caffeine and drinking even one cup of strong tea or coffee in the afternoon inevitably caused a few hours of staring at the ceiling after midnight. Chocolate has a similar effect: even a small piece of dark chocolate consumed later in the day can cause insomnia. Interestingly, green tea often gave me the most intense heart palpitation, even worse than I would get from coffee.

I think all this sensitivity is individual; I just had to observe my body's reaction. Now, being acutely aware of every anxiety symptom, I know that a cup of regular coffee or tea may bring on heart palpitations. I love the taste, so on occasion I "bite the bullet" and go for that strong cup of java, knowing that in twenty minutes or so I may feel my heart racing.

When I choose to drink anything with caffeine in it, I know what the possible side effects are, so it does not surprise me if my heart starts to race after I indulge in a delicious latte or cappuccino. To my great relief, I noticed that after a series of recent acupuncture treatments, my sensitivity to caffeine diminished, which was a pleasant surprise.

Sugar

Sugar and other refined carbohydrates cause mood swings in many people. I still need to observe this closely to see how strongly my body reacts and what other dietary factors are involved. Low blood sugar can cause symptoms of anxiety to surface, but stress may also cause drop in blood sugar and it can create a vicious circle. The connection between the body's biochemistry and stress is incredible. Symptoms of anxiety and hypoglycemia (rapid drop in blood sugar) are quite similar: light-headedness and weakness to a point of trembling, as well as palpitations. When I indulge in too many sweets (around the holidays when they are a constant temptation), I may experience sudden hunger surges, with strong hypoglycemia as my body overproduces insulin. A simultaneous production of excessive adrenaline and cortisol causes increased anxiety symptoms. As I learned to limit and then eliminate refined sugar from my diet (except for the occasional treat), I've noticed positive change. After a while, the related hunger surges and unpleasant symptoms ceased. Refraining from consuming refined carbohydrates, dairy that has lactose (a form of sugar in milk) takes inner strength but is well worth it! Prolonged periods of clean diet have many health benefits, including weight loss (a favorite of the vain), relief from pain, allergy symptoms, sinus infections and resilience to viruses.

Good news: chocolate promotes the production of serotonin. Bad news: sugar and dairy in milk chocolate are too high and counteract the benefits. Dark chocolate is an acquired taste for many of us, but eating about one ounce a day delivers the mood-boosting we need.

Bottom line: friends should not let friends eat too much sugar. Now I try not to bring a customary cake or other baked dessert to a party or when visiting a friend, but opt for flowers, dark chocolate, fruit and nuts.

Alcohol

Many revert to having a drink or two when seeking fast relief from stress. It certainly helps to temporarily alter moods and dissolve pain and sorrow. At times, all it took was a few sips of wine to ease the pain I had inside. But this "friend" can quickly become an enemy with carelessness.

I talked to my doctor about drinking alcohol as a means to relieve stress. She agreed that a glass of wine may be better than medication with less side effects if it is drunk occasionally and in moderation, otherwise it can be harmful. An occasional glass of red wine can even be beneficial due to unique antioxidant polyphenol compounds found in grape skin and seeds, but more than that may cause anxiety due to inflammation caused by excessive alcohol consumption. Drinking too much does more harm than good. Many people choose not to drink alcohol at all and can take supplements with grape seed or grape skin extracts to reap the benefits of these powerful antioxidants. I was much better off not drinking at all. Also, when I was taking anti-anxiety medication, drinking alcohol was not allowed. Alcohol seems to be a cheap alternative when the affordability of acupuncture, massage, naturopathic doctors and psychologists is an issue. But these providers may be covered by medical insurance, as well as regular doctor visits and conventional anti-anxiety medications. The thing is to find and use qualified professional help. It is imperative to recognize the effects of stress on human body and the need to address it in timely manner. In order to get out of stress-induced emotional tailspins, we need to equip ourselves with knowledge of preventative and coping measures to live healthy and fulfilled lives.

The Vicious Cycle of Comfort Food

I read articles and books on healthy living, but what was feasible for me? When I was on a strict diet in an attempt to get rid of mysterious stomach pain, my anxiety level subsided significantly and I noticed other health benefits. But to achieve that, I had to quit sugar, very sweet fruit as well as some vegetables, dairy products, fried food, baked goods and pasta, alcohol and caffeine. Though extremely challenging, as I love good food and chafe at such restriction, this regimen was invaluable. I haven't been able to sustain this diet indefinitely, even a modified version. It was great for my health, alright, but let me say it again: I *love* food!

Luckily, I never cared too much for sweets, though on rare occasions I could eat a box of chocolates or half a cake if it hits my taste buds—or if I am desperate! Thankfully, I am quite picky with sweets. On the other hand, savory treats, especially cheeses and nuts, were always my favorite. Give this girl a plate of cheese, fruit and nuts, accompanied by a glass of red wine (or even tea) and I am a happy camper. I like to cook and I often crave rich comfort food. Whenever I eat sensibly, I feel better overall, so I need to remind myself of the definite health benefits of discipline. Listening to CDs on healthy eating or reading a book on this subject is a good way to do it.

Alkaline

Many vitamins and supplements are not properly absorbed if the body is highly acidic. An alkaline-forming diet is highly beneficial, as I have seen in myself. There are lists of alkaline or antacid diets online. Some of the items are contradictory (like tomatoes or oatmeal), but many items are consistently listed as either alkaline or acid forming foods.

One of the ways to increase alkalinity is to drink plenty of plain water with a splash of lemon juice or apple cider vinegar. It sounds strange, as it tastes sour, but it actually reduces acidity level in the body.

I've become a regular at local juice bars (I live in the Los Angeles area where they pop up like mushrooms after a rain), but much cheaper versions can be made at home. My go-to staple is a green juice. With slight variation, it's a mix of fresh spinach, celery, cucumber, kale, cabbage, lemon, ginger and apple. It is very refreshing and I really like the way I feel after drinking it. There are times when I would drink one a day for a few days, but usually it's a once-a-week deal. I don't think drinking too much concentrated greens every day is what I should be doing.

Lastly, I remember the advice I read somewhere—to limit CATS- caffeine, alcohol, tobacco and sugar. As tobacco is not an issue for me anymore, I replaced "T" in this word with trans fats—something to avoid in my diet as well. I also added BSM: breathe, smile and move.

We Are What We Eat

In order to stay alive, we need to eat live food. I don't mean live animals or bugs, but fresh food that didn't come from a can or a box. Often we don't get enough necessary nutrients from what we eat. We can add supplements, but we cannot rely solely on them, otherwise they wouldn't be supplementing, they would be supplanting.

❝ *In order to stay alive, we need to eat live food*

Meat products (especially processed), dairy products, sugar, fruit with high sugar content, fruit juice, baked goods and pasta should be on my plate only once in a while. What is left? Actually, there is a lot, but most of us don't even know what to do with all those parsnips, turnips, sweet potatoes and cauliflower florets! Thankfully there are many recipes in cookbooks, magazines and online. My friends also share their favorite recipes on social media and I like to try them. "Seek and you shall find". My commitment to eat better enabled me to find a way to do it. There are tons of spices waiting to be discovered which make meals more nutritious and flavorful, as well as delicious fruit and vegetables ready for picking, even if only at a local market.

When we know how many benefits for our health are hidden in produce, we may look at them differently. Let's take bell peppers, for instance. Thanks to vitamin C and other compounds eating this vegetable cuts down cortisol level. Broccoli, cauliflower, cabbage and other cruciferous veggies help metabolize excess estrogen that in turn can curb anxiety. They also aid in detoxifying. Red cabbage is especially rich in powerful antioxidants that help producing mood-elevating hormones.

All great foods can be found at fresh fruit and vegetable aisles at the supermarket. Preferably, the produce should be organically grown.

Recent studies show a definite connection between the lack of friendly gut bacteria and emotions. Taking prescribed antibiotics wipes out beneficial intestinal flora in a matter of days, so taking probiotic supplements is very important after being treated with antibiotics. Consuming food that has been treated with antibiotics affects digestion as well, even if more gradually. Unfortunately, most of mass-produced meat and fish has been treated with antibiotics or hormones. Free-range chickens, grass-fed beef and wild-caught fish have much less harmful substances in their flesh. I prefer all-organic diet, even if it is more expensive. If I have more fruit and vegetables in my diet with less meat and very sweet fruit, I feel more energetic and vibrant. If I cannot avoid antibiotics, I begin eating yogurt, sauerkraut and other fermented vegetables or supplement with probiotic supplements, all of which helps to restore the gut balance.

I found a lot of good advice on eating right. Numerous books and articles are available: I just need to choose and follow. The challenging part is to stick to a healthy diet. I like reminding myself of beneficial eating habits, so I read as well as listen to subject-related books.

PART THREE

SOUL SEARCH

CHAPTER TWELVE

Integrating Theology and Psychology

> *"We are Physical, Mental and Spiritual beings.*
> *If you don't deal with ALL OF LIFE,*
> *you're not going to get all that life has to offer."*
> *Zig Ziglar*

Through Wilderness to Enlightenment

The word "enlightenment" is used to describe all kinds of spiritual "illumination." People seeking the Divine often use it to explain their experiences. As for so many of us, suffering and distress forced me to go on a deep spiritual journey. I had to go into this "wilderness" to emerge stronger and better equipped for battles life undoubtedly will have for me in the future. I am very social by nature, yet I needed solitude to have deep conversations with God—to pray and to listen. I had to learn to be still and dwell in the Divine presence without feeling guilty for doing "nothing." Being still for me became an act of obedience, not laziness. I learned to keep my priorities in check (well, most of the time...) and not feel guilty for "wasting time" in stillness and recuperation.

Dividing the Secular and Spiritual

I try not to divide spiritual and practical aspects of my life. Many people look for a practical approach to getting rid of pain and don't like getting too deep into spiritual issues. Somewhere along the way they got disillusioned about God and all things spiritual, or they don't see the importance of soul-searching and the connection between our well-being and the Divine. It is very unfortunate, and as a former atheist, I know how empty one feels when they don't feel and don't see the signs of Divine presence and don't acknowledge miracles in their lives.

❝ *The Lord created me as a spiritual being in a physical body, which is a temple for His spirit*

When my innermost being is troubled and my very soul is in distress, I instinctively cry out to God. I seek the counsel of man on many occasions but I have no illusion that fallible humans have all the answers. For example, I love chatting with girlfriends, complaining about how miserable I might feel, but they are not capable of "fixing" my problems. Many of my friends are not Christian, but I never hide my beliefs from our conversations. It is easier for me to talk about spiritual aspects with those who can relate to such things, even though I tried to share with non-believers. I try not to act differently with my church-going Christian friends and non-believers, but there are certain things that non-believers do not see, thus it is difficult for them to identify with. They may not be able to comprehend how I communicate with God, but I am always willing to explain and share my experiences.

When I shared about my walk with God through anxiety and was open about other aspects of my spiritual walk and miracles I witnessed, I willingly opened up to the possibility of being misunderstood and ridiculed. It did not stop me from opening up and sharing. I am not afraid to be vulnerable. I hunger for spirit-filled in-depth conversations with my friends, I want to share the experience of closeness with God I had on many occasions, but it is difficult to get through. I can imagine being talked of behind my back: Look at this goody two shoes, who does she think she is, a saint? She is "talking to God", really! Just look at some of her actions! Yes, I am not a saint, not even close, but I want to walk with God and please Him with what I do or say and I try. I've gotten better over the years, though I am not where I want to be in my spiritual walk. For a person who was raised in a predominantly atheistic society, it is still pretty good, I think. I love my non-Christian friends and I wish they could experience the joy of closeness with God I experience and feel the amazing power of praying together and for each other. Interestingly, some people may mock our love for God but be thankful for prayers offered on their behalf. I regularly pray for my friends, believers and non-believers alike. We all need the grace and mercy of God.

I was a non-believer myself once, but I was a seeker. My upbringing in the atheistic society of the Soviet Union did not stick with me for too long. I had this void in my heart I was not able to fill, no matter what I tried. It took years but I finally realized that what I was missing was a deep connection with God. The Lord created me as a spiritual being in a physical body, which is a temple for His spirit. It is with His guidance that I continue to strive to live a happy, healthy and fulfilling life, asking for wisdom along the way.

Spirituality as Experience, Not Doctrine

I think it is okay to question God, which is better than to doubt Him or to reject Him altogether. Being honest with God, having a conversation with Him and approaching Him with one's deepest questions is a quest to understanding and growth. Inquiring of God is normal, and He answers in a variety of ways: through other people, through His word in the Bible, through insights, dreams, intuition and visions. Experiencing pain strengthened my faith, which, in turn, gave me perseverance to find answers, courage to be vulnerable and strength to push forward. The power of this momentum and conversations with God gave me hope to see the bright and joyous future ahead, to seek fulfillment of my life's purpose.

I strongly believe that God allows things to occur for His divine purpose

God's Plan

I am indeed fulfilling my purpose and discovering little by little what that looks like. I strongly believe that God allows things to occur for His divine purpose. What I once saw as obstacles in my life I now see as a means to deliver me from trouble or to lead me to fuller life, through correction. God uses our emotional pain to mature us, and I see now that God had a Master Plan for my life all along and nothing happened without His knowledge. For us, it is hard if not impossible to see the whole picture, so we get frustrated. I longed to look back and make sense of all my pain and suffering. I rejoice that such a time came. For those who seek wisdom, this time comes as great revelation. Pain, misfortune and disease may be used by God in our lives to slow us down, to encourage repentance, to turn our eyes on Him, to show who is the Creator and who is not, to reveal our ignorance and force us to rely solely on Him. We cannot fully comprehend His divine purpose, and it is different in every particular case, but if we are blessed with insight, we will look back and see God's hand in all events that occurred, regardless of immediate outcome. I believe that God is love, it is His very essence. It is not what He does but what He is. He does everything in love. I think even when He is judging our deeds, He does so in love.

One of my favorite passages in the Bible comes from the Book of Isaiah 26:3: *"You will keep in perfect peace those whose minds are steadfast, because they trust in you."*

> **God does not promise us that we are exempt from suffering, but when we go through times of trouble, He will walk with us**

I Am Not in Control, God Is

Trusting God to be in control makes the difference between hope and hopelessness. Relying on my Creator brings comfort, a sense of stability and purpose, even in the most complicated and stressful situations. Of course, I didn't come to this realization overnight. I tried to solve my problems by relying on my own strength. My reasoning varied between not wanting to bother God with my sorry little problems, to bouts of extreme self-confidence bordering on self-centeredness. The result was pitiful, to say the least. Interestingly, when I jumped into action without consulting God first, I didn't always fail right away. But later, after encountering numerous obstacles, I inevitably realized that with God's help, everything would have flowed much better, not always easier, but better in the long run. Plus, I won't be tempted to take credit for the achievement. I eventually learned to give up control. I wish I learned the lesson sooner—I would have saved myself from much heartache. I wonder why this elusive sense of control is so important to us? We hold on to it with all our might without realizing how pitiful such attempts really are.

Glory to Me or Glory to God: Humbling Myself

All of these lessons took place for a reason. We only truly learn by going through adversity. My Creator has the power to give me strength and knowledge to overcome any obstacle. I learned to solely rely on God when I was going through trials and tribulations. I am still learning to let the Lord guide me because I'm inclined to do everything in my own strength, especially when I am well physically and all seems to be okay. In our fast changing world, He is the unchanging one. God does not promise us that we are exempt from suffering, but when we go through times of trouble, He will walk with us. This is exactly what He did when he was walking with Shadrach, Meshach and Abednego in a fiery furnace. He also promised in the book of Isaiah that *when* we go through trouble, He would be with us. Yes, that's right, <u>when</u>. We will have a lot of difficult situations in this world, but it's how we go through them and whom we rely on that makes the difference.

My Journey to Faith

If twenty years ago anyone had told me that I would write this book, I would not have believed him, so impossible did it seem.

❝ *I desire to build a beautiful, meaningful and deep relationship with God*

I was born in Kiev, Ukraine. At the time it was not an independent country but was one of fifteen "soviet socialist republics" that formed the Soviet Union—"Russia" as many westerners referred to it. Like millions of children there, I was raised an atheist. Growing up, I didn't think about God much, nor did I imagine that the Lord would interfere, transform me into a believer, drastically change my life and eventually bring me to California. What a wild ride it has been!

During my childhood, going to church and believing in God was not only ridiculed but also full of negative consequences. It lasted until I graduated college and became a teacher. My first years as a public school teacher were in the late eighties. I remember attending a teachers meeting around Easter, when a school principal was assigning to teachers the "church duty" of going to a local Russian Orthodox church to detect whether any of the students were attending service. If detected, students and their parents would be in serious trouble. Bolsheviks destroyed many churches after the Revolution of 1917. The ones that survived were stripped of their former glory, vandalized, robbed and converted to storage buildings, barns or community centers. Priceless frescos were destroyed, plastered or painted over. A few churches remained open for believers. The Soviet government wanted to demonstrate to the world that religious freedom existed in the Soviet Union, but it was a facade. If people were seen attending services regularly and actually worshiping God, they could have been reported and persecuted, or so I was taught in school and at home. Therefore, regular church attendance could not be a good thing. When I went to church on occasion, I listened to beautiful singing, would light a candle and look at beautiful frescos and icons around me. There were some very beautiful churches in Kiev and I liked wandering into them now and then.

" Relying on my Creator brings comfort, a sense of stability and purpose, even in the most complicated and stressful situations

Only a few years after I had begun teaching, Perestroika opened the door to religious freedom. People were searching for God and ironically, the same school principal led a group of teachers and students in a pilgrimage to a famous monastery called Pochayevska Lavra in Western Ukraine. It was a major milestone in our history.

At approximately the same time, YWAM (Youth With A Mission) visited the school where my brother was a senior. Eventually. he went to YWAM Bible School, became a part of their team, went on mission trips to build houses in Crimea and even evangelized in the streets of Istanbul. For the latter, he was thrown into Turkish prison. Thankfully, he spent only one night there and had a ticket to fly back to Ukraine the following day. My brother didn't tell anybody in the family so as not to alarm us. I learned about this ordeal while sitting in church one Sunday morning. By then, Calvary Chapel planted one of their churches in Kiev and there I was, listening to my baby brother telling about his mission trip. Actually, it was my brother who kept inviting me to church. I would join him on occasion and whenever the call was made for salvation, I would freeze in my seat. How can I be forgiven, me—a filthy sinner? I was so ashamed of all the shameful things I did in the past. But finally the desire to know God outgrew the fear and other negative emotions. I want to compare this experience to that of a frightened little stray kitten, sitting in a dumpster in the rain. All of a sudden, a warm loving hand picked it up and brought it home. There this kitten was fed, washed, dried and put on a nice soft pillow just to stay, enjoy and bring a smile to the face of its Master.

My life began to change, with the greatest change occurring in my mind and character, which were strengthened and edified. Many of my choices and actions then became empowered with God's guidance. My life didn't turn 180 degrees right away, but the transformation was significant. I definitely was not the same anymore. Miracles were happening left and right, which further strengthened my faith. Was I still tempted on many occasions? You better believe it. As a matter of fact, I often still am.

Actually, my path to believing in God started much earlier, when I was about thirteen years old. Then the Lord touched my heart in a very interesting way. My Mom was on a trip for almost a month and I stayed with my Dad. It was very dramatic, as I was used to having Mom around all the time. One night I could not go to sleep and was just lying in bed with my eyes open. I did not want to be in the dark, so I didn't draw the curtains. A streetlight was shining on the wall right in front of me. There an image of Jesus was hanging, hidden from view. My father was a communist, so this image of Jesus, an old family heirloom, was obscure. It was not thrown away, thankfully, because my family respected this memento of our ancestors. I wondered why it was not hidden in a closet. I do think coincidences are miracles in disguise. We only call them so because we are unable to comprehend God's power and plan for our lives. I think that night the Lord used the old icon that was vaguely sparkling of gold and lit from a streetlight. The Lord revealed Himself to me. I spontaneously began to pray. My family didn't have a Bible at our apartment and no one ever taught me how to pray. Nor did I tell anyone about that experience. Nevertheless, since that night I would pray every night for my family and friends. It began with simple, innocent and sincere prayers of a youth. I prayed like that every night for years without telling a soul, as I was afraid to be ridiculed. Years later I became a follower of Christ, but lost this habit of regular praying. However, my relationship with God became more personal and intimate as I began talking to Him as to a person. I remember the main character from "Fiddler on the Roof." This man was talking to God on a regular basis, not as a formal prayer, but as a genuine, ongoing conversation.

❝ My relationship with God became more personal and intimate as I began talking to Him as to a person

Drifting Away from God

I wish that I had dwelt in the Lord's presence ever since I became a believer but it was not like that. At times I didn't feel Him being there with me. Sometimes I hoped He was not looking when I was doing wrong and knew it. I still walk with God one step at a time. I want to follow the dreams He has planted in my heart. With childlike faith and excitement one week, I may be cold and indifferent the next. Everyday responsibilities and challenges got in the way. How I wish to be raised in a picture-perfect Christian home, raised on the Word of God, in the habit of worship and the power of prayer. It was not so, and learning became a long process. I had to catch up. It is very challenging to change your ways completely when you are an adult, but with God, all things are possible. Unfortunately, often God took a "backseat" when I got busy with my daily life and drifted away from in-depth relationship with Him. My focus also shifted from God to survival on numerous occasions when I was battling serious illness or awaiting surgeries. Later I wondered if I was being punished for my actions when I later suffered this so-called mental illness. Of course, with acquired wisdom I learned that God does not punish, but suffering caused me to reflect on times that I walked away from God. Business caused me to make decisions that led me astray, little by little, until I found myself in the turmoil of desperation and in a spiritual desert, when I did not feel the Lord's presence in my life. It felt as though all my prayers were falling on deaf ears, and I had used up all my blessings, that my Heavenly Father turned away from me for good. But the Lord was gracious to take me back every time, "never leaving nor forsaking me," even when I felt that He had.

I learned to ask myself if my actions and words please and glorify God. I like it to be a habit and part of my every morning: to have a cup of coffee or tea and ask myself what can I do today to please God with my words and actions. It is impossible to be perfect, but I want to try to live a God-pleasing life.

It took a while, but it finally began to sink in—we are created for worship. Worship for me is not only singing, it reflects my words and actions as well. It is a great challenge to live one's life as an act of worship to her Creator.

Relationship with God—The First Love

Throughout my life, I would get closer to some people and then we'd grow apart. Sometimes years would pass and we'd reconnect again. For years my relationship with God had a similar dynamic. I had different seasons with God. In my growth process, the relationship with God deepened, but then there were times when I put Him aside. I was slowly maturing in the Lord and He foresaw the progressive stages of it with all its ups and downs, curves and ditches.

❝ When I first found the beauty of a relationship with God I was overjoyed

Falling in love with a person for the first time is a beautiful feeling. Have you ever fallen in love? Do you remember how it felt in the very beginning? You can't stop thinking about this person, you want to spend every waking moment with him or her. Similarly, when I first found the beauty of a relationship with God, I was overjoyed. Unfortunately from my experience, the dynamic of that "first love," with a person and even with God, wears off and I fall into a relationship of routine. This feeling of fresh love we often miss later in a relationship. Many married people are in search of rediscovering such thrill of head over heels excitement, when we can't wait to spend time with the beloved. They may even begin looking elsewhere in hope of experiencing this amazing feeling again.

Now I see a definite similarity between my relationship with God and my other relationships. As with so many people, at first I was trying to learn to establish relationships and friendships with people and only later in life came to realize that I need to learn more about relationship with God: how to establish it, how to communicate, how to listen. This relationship, unlike the earthly ones, is eternal. I want to figure out how to do it right. We reap what we sow into relationship, and many know how much work a successful marriage takes. I find that the same attention is due God, but even more so, as He takes precedence over all. So if I got upset with God, it was I who was not spending enough time with Him, nor was I listening to what He was saying. Man, I think I was not listening half the time! I need to learn communication skills: when and how to speak and when and how to listen.

When I was not physically and emotionally well, my main concern was to get better. It was hard to focus on questions such as, "Do my actions please and glorify my Creator?" or "What can I do today to fulfill my life's purpose?" Instead, I was pleading to get well, preferably fast. When a major destruction like a disease, disaster or grief strikes, our focus often shifts into human survival mode. I wish I was trained and prepared from childhood for right actions at such times. Firefighters train extensively before they ever face real fire. Fighter pilots spend hours and hours in classrooms, on flight simulators and just flying before they ever face real combat. I was not trained in overcoming obstacles God's way in childhood, but I was allowed to learn later in life. In the midst of severe mental disturbance ravaging my poor weary body, I was like a lonely child, desperately looking for comfort and love. I realized that only connection with God could fully satisfy such a longing.

I desire to build a beautiful, meaningful and deep relationship with God. It was always easier for me to get closer to God when I wasn't working full-time or everything was relatively peaceful in my extended family, allowing me to focus on building this relationship with my Creator. I need to keep my priorities in check, not allowing unimportant things to take priority. Running errands and doing chores after work are important but nurturing relationships with family and friends are crucial. Unfortunately, I often put my to-do list first, becoming exhausted and resentful. When I lose energy, I succumb to emotions. My relationships with loved ones reflect my relationship with my Heavenly Father more than I want to admit. Waiting until bedtime to spend time with the Lord means that I may be snoozing before I utter a word of gratitude or open my Bible.

We seek to gaze at the face of the one we love. We fall in love with that person's face, don't we? I want to seek the face of the Lord, His perfect will for my life. My life needs to be God-centered all the time.

Without time spent nurturing a relationship, why be surprised if we are growing apart? In our dependent shortsightedness, we cry out to God in desperation, but otherwise may forget Him.

With the long-distance relationship, you would give anything just to get a glimpse of your beloved, who occupies your mind 24/7. But do I clear out my schedule to spend time with Him? Do I calendar a "date night" where I only listen, pray and dwell in His presence, undistracted by the business of daily life, or do I give Him only the leftovers of my time? His presence in my daily life refreshes and rejuvenates me, and I tap into abundant joy and peace when I earnestly seek Him.

CHAPTER THIRTEEN

Is It Possible To Justify Suffering?

"At the end of that time, I, Nebuchadnezzar,
raised my eyes toward heaven,
and my sanity was restored.
Then I praised the Most High;
I honored and glorified him who lives forever."
Daniel 4:34

Psychology vs. Faith

It still shocks me every time I hear an argument against the need of clinical psychology. It is especially disappointing when in this day and age some Christians still argue that when someone suffers from mental torment, all such persons need is to pray and repent. I heard it again just the other day, expressed by a well—educated person! I am glad I had an opportunity to express my point of view based on personal experiences. Thankfully, after our conversation, my opponent altered her opinion. But it left me wondering how many well-wishing people there are who perceive a spiritual attack as the only explanation for mental disorder. There are people who believe that, rather than turn to doctors or medicine, we should put all our healing needs in God's hands by petition and prayer only. They go so far as to deny medical help altogether, especially if it is about mental illness. These people need to be educated, sooner than later. Thankfully, the majority realizes that treating mental conditions with medication, supplements and therapy is a way to correct chemical imbalance and speed up the healing process.

" *There is worry that we can choose to stop and then there is an anxiety attack that is rooted in biochemical processes in the physical body*

I do believe that God is almighty and all-powerful, able to remove sickness from anyone's body once and for all. Jesus ' performed numerous healing miracles, but he did not heal all. We live in a fallen world, infested with sin and, as a result, suffering. The Lord may choose to allow us to go through pain and suffering, for the possible purpose of growth, reflection and to be drawn into a closer relationship with Him. The extreme measures of using sickness and suffering as a means to correct my behavior are possible, but I sure hope that chances of God going to such drastic measures in my life are miniscule. I choose to believe that on most occasions, pain does not come into my life as punishment nor are pleasure and good fortune given to me as a reward for my flawless actions. In Russian, a mentally ill person is often referred to as "soul sick," and there is some truth to this expression. The disconnection such a person experiences between his mind, body and soul is excruciating and confusing.

Sanity Check or Sanitizing My Mind

I once heard it said by a pastor that anxiety is sinful. Wait a minute! For a sufferer of severe panic attacks, to hear that was brutal. I know that I prayed, I fasted, I begged God for deliverance again and again, but it didn't happen right away. I then thought there should have been some other reason for this wrenching pain in my chest, and it propelled the quest to healing and as a result, the writing of this book.

" *I believe when God allows things to happen in our lives, it is ultimately for the sake of a greater good and often happens for purpose of our learning and growth*

I believe when someone talks about sinfulness of anxiety, they're talking about over-thinking and worry, not actual panic attacks. There is worry that we can choose to stop and then there is an anxiety attack that is rooted in biochemical processes in the physical body. When I speak publicly and explain what I went through, perhaps people with harsh opinions about mental disorders without experiencing its turmoil will change their minds. This has happened in the past. I am on a mission to educate people about this issue.

If God created heaven and earth and the whole of humanity, He surely has the power to cure me. I firmly believe in miracles and His healing power. Why He does not heal everyone is hard to understand, but not for me to decide. I believe when God allows things to happen in our lives, it is ultimately for the sake of a greater good and often happens for the purpose of our learning and growth. I learned in the process to face my fears instead of running from them or letting them overwhelm me. My attitude towards my life and experiences defines me as child of Almighty God. I tended to immediately become the problem-solver when facing obstacles. I learned to pause, pray and listen. Maybe acting impulsively is not required.

The Ultimate Physician

I began to approach the understanding of sickness, misfortune and healing in a new way. The Lord can heal on the spot, and when He does not do so, it must be for a reason. His ways are unbeknown to man and we all are mortal. Even the great prophet Elisha, who performed amazing miracles, including bringing the dead back to life, *"was suffering from the illness from which he died".* *(2 Kings 13:14).* Healing ministries with the laying on of hands, casting out demons, and praying in tongues are foreign to many, but there are many witnesses to prove that miracles do happen as a result of such spiritual intervention. I am a firm believer in miracles, having witnessed many firsthand. Unfortunately, not every prayer is immediately answered and not every person gets healed. After all, as much as we refuse to accept it, our human bodies are mortal. God can choose to heal me or not, but either way, His will ultimately will be done.

We should not look at our diseases and misfortunes as punishment from above. Yes, on rare occasion God allows such things to happen in our lives as a means of correction for disobedience and misbehavior, as implied in Hebrews 12. We need to do our part of soul-searching and cleaning, repenting of all wrongdoing. More often than not, our merciful God wants to give us healing regardless of what we've done. He is the God Who Heals. Don't stop asking for healing. In 2 Kings 20:1-7 God sent Isaiah to King Hezekiah with a message to put his affairs in order because the king was going to die. Hezekiah cried out to God, asking to postpone his death, reminding his Creator of his faithfulness. It worked! God sent Isaiah back to the king with a new verdict. He was given fifteen more years of life. Miracle? Yes. Does it happen every time? No.

Insanity or Mental Conditions in the Bible

There are Biblical examples of insanity: King Saul chasing after David, throwing a spear at him from time to time—by no means a rational behavior! On occasion, King David, "a man after God's own heart" cried to The Lord (Psalm 143): *"I am paralyzed with fear!" and "Come quickly, Lord, and answer me, for my depression deepens".*

King Nebuchadnezzar, acting and living like an animal for seven long years, enduring punishment for his pride. These men were powerful kings appointed by God, regardless of their human nature and mental conditions. God had a plan for every one of them. Let's take a closer look.

A Story of King Nebuchadnezzar

A long time ago in a far-away land lived King Nebuchadnezzar. One day he awoke from a dream by which he was so disturbed he could not even recall it! Have you ever awoken from sleep, not being able to recall your dream, yet feeling it was something big and important? King Neb called all his astrologers and dream interpreters and charged them to not only to interpret his dream, but also to first describe it to him. Nobody was able to do it, except one person, who trusted and worshipped the one and only God Almighty. This man's name was Daniel, and with God he was able to help the king.

It turned out in this dream, the king was warned about upcoming disasters and was able to avoid dire consequences by listening to God-given interpretation. Unfortunately, even after realizing how powerful God was, King Neb decided to take credit for his achievements and wealth. Big mistake, huge gaffe! As a means of correction of this prideful behavior, God had given him the mind of a beast for a season. Thankfully, there was a plan for Neb's life, so God restored him completely to full power. Never did Nebuchadnezzar have such a slip-up again.

Not that I'm a queen, but was God also humbling me for a season? Thankfully, I was not on hands and knees, hanging out with wild donkeys, but I was reduced to a quivering mess at times, completely undone. Was the Lord Almighty allowing this to happen, until I, like King Neb, realized the sovereignty of the Most

High God, who humbled my heart? I was released from pride and began to give praise and glory to my Creator.

Daniel's Example

Another character in King Neb's story was the prophet Daniel. From him I learned quite a few things. He had a habit of praying three times a day on his knees, always beginning with thanksgiving. We may argue that Daniel was a single young man, not a mother, wife, an executive with a tight schedule... I may think it was easier for him to make time to have a diligent prayer life, three times a day at appointed times. However, Daniel was a king's servant with things to do. Actually, remaining loyal to his God caused him to be persecuted for his faith. As a result of his faithfulness, Daniel remained fearless in times of trouble. In imminent, life-threatening danger, he simply prayed and went to sleep, even on the eve of being thrown into the lion's den!

❝ *I wish it were not so, but unfortunately, this is how we grow the most—through trials and sorrow*

I always have fresh revelation from Daniel as to the role of thanksgiving in my life; that my day should begin and end with gratitude. Not only is God responsive to a grateful heart, being grateful changes my whole attitude towards life and its challenges.

When I am facing my own "lions," do I trust my God completely? Am I disciplined to pray like that? Not yet, but God is taking me from "glory to glory" by conforming me into the image of His Son, Jesus. Daniel sure is a great role model. Influenced by his prayer life, I utter prayers throughout the day: big, small and tiny. *"I lean and rely and confidently trust in Him,"* as it is written in Psalm 91. And then I forget to pray for something major and try to solve it on my own. Sound stupid? You bet! But when desperation hits, I cry, I plead, I beg. I ask "why me?" and "why now?" And then: "please don't let me be crazy", "please don't let me die now," usually followed by " If you do this, Lord, I will be a really good girl and..." some promises I keep, some of them, I'm ashamed to admit, are never to be fulfilled...yet "He knows my frame" and He loves me just the same.

Suffering in the Bible

Suffering: too many know how it feels and it comes in various unpleasant shapes and forms. It is somewhat comforting to know that many people whose life journeys are described in the Bible endured hardship. I feel this way not because "misery loves company" but because I can learn from such examples and be encouraged to keep pressing on toward my God-given Destiny.

The Bible basically guarantees pain and suffering in our lives—it's just a matter of time. How well are we equipped to withstand such curveballs life inevitably throws at us is a very good question to ponder. We need to be prepared.

Who wants to learn from pain and suffering? Raise your hands! Nobody? What a surprise! I wish it were not so, but unfortunately, this is how we grow the most—through trials and sorrow. Great men in the Bible were no exception.

Job

Job in one day was turned from the wealthiest and happiest man of his time into a sick, lonely and desperate person. His story, which describes his unwavering faith in God and journey to complete restoration, is one of my favorites. In the end, not only his health and fortune were restored, they were doubled. He also was blessed with more children. I read somewhere that his youngest daughters were named Peace, Fragrance and Beauty—what a metaphor for beautiful blossoms that can grow from pain and suffering. It reminds me of a promise from the prophet

Jeremiah, God's assurance to His people to give them a crown of beauty for ashes.

King David

King David was running from King Saul for years, expressing his feelings of anguish and despair in the best journal of all times— the Psalms. He trusted God completely, regardless of his often dire circumstances.

Joseph

Joseph was sold into slavery by his own brothers. After he was taken to a foreign country, it seemed he had a break. Joseph was favored by his master and appointed as manager of a huge estate. Not long after, he was wrongly accused by his owner's wife of attempted rape and thrown in jail. *"Until the time came to fulfill his dreams, the Lord tested Joseph's character." Psalm 105:19 (NLT)* Thankfully, it all turned for better, as he was appointed a ruler of Egypt, second only to Pharaoh himself, was reunited with his brothers, whom he forgave, and his father. He lived to the ripe old age of one hundred and ten.

Apostle Paul

The Apostle Paul wrote about his sufferings: *"Therefore, in order to keep me from becoming conceited, I was given a thorn in my flesh, a messenger of Satan, to torment me. Three times I pleaded with the Lord to take it away from me. But he said to me, "My grace is sufficient for you, for my power is made perfect in weakness." Therefore I will boast all the more gladly about my weaknesses, so that Christ's power may rest on me. That is why, for Christ's sake, I delight in weaknesses, in insults, in hardships, in persecutions, in difficulties. For when I am weak, then I am strong." 2 Corinthians 12:7–10*

The Apostle Paul's letter to the Philippians is one of my favorite biblical epistles. It's famous quote "I can do all things through Him who gives me strength" is very encouraging to all God's people, and especially to those who suffer a great deal, as these words were written in prison. The whole passage talks about relying on God in the midst of disastrous storms that happen in life. Gratitude regardless of circumstances is the key. To a grateful heart, love and grace begin to flow, as if heavenly faucets have opened up. When I am not diligent with gratitude, I can quickly become dried out. I need to be filled with joy and appreciation daily, even if writing my gratitude in a journal or whispering them to my God first thing in the morning.

Pleasing God with my words and actions is my goal. Regardless of challenges I face and obstacles I am to overcome, I am still God's beloved child. I am here for a reason and my Creator is in control of it all. Let His will be done. He promised that He would bring to completion good works He began in my life. He will do the same in yours. Amen to that!

Seeking Joy

Finding meaning in my suffering, reframing it as a learning experience with which to help others, and seeking joy became my quest. I consciously try to enjoy life to the fullest. I look for beauty in creation around me. I cultivate love within me. I may have difficult circumstances, face various challenges and obstacles, yet I must remember I am here for a reason and I was created with purpose. It is up to me to seek guidance from my Lord and Savior, discover and strive to fulfill it. I might as well learn to enjoy the process of daily living, challenges, difficulties, struggles and all.

Even in the darkest times, I didn't hesitate to ask God for joy. I did it even when it sounded like an outrageous request. Getting joyous in the midst of an "episode" didn't always come to mind, but when it did, I prayed, pleading for the seemingly unthinkable. When I suffer, often all I want is just to feel better. Asking for joy under such circumstances seems like a big stretch of faith, but I realize it's not. This joy I asked for seldom replaced anxiety quickly, but when it was finally granted, my heart sang in gratitude. Sometime it took quite a while to reach this place of complete immersion in Glory. Thankfully there are so many Scriptures that encourage me to seek joy in the darkest hours. Handy Internet search to the rescue: "Joy" "God" "Bible" and voila! Encouraging scriptures appear on a screen. Choose, print, savor, memorize, and use daily. God's promises are always encouraging and refreshing for mind, body and soul as this triad is interwoven on so many levels.

Asking God for a miracle of joy became one of my favorites when I pray for others or for myself. The way to achieve pure joy is to seek God's presence and by pleasing Him in doing what I was created to do. I realize that happiness is circumstantial when joy is a gift from above. Joy is a condition of one's heart.

For some, helping others to ease their suffering can become the highest calling in life. I am compelled to cry and pray with people who are going through pain and emotional distress, for God asks us to "bear others' burdens", which is done through prayer and listening. *"Anxiety in a man's heart weighs him down, but a good word makes him glad." Proverbs 12:25 (ESV).* I like to ask God for divine appointments, then wait and see whom He will send my way. It happens to be one of those prayers that are answered time and again, maybe because it is not self-centered. Quite often He sends my way someone who needs help, advice, prayer, or all of the above. Helping others, especially those in trouble, gives meaning to an otherwise egotistical existence.

CHAPTER FOURTEEN

Dialogues With God

*"Be anxious for nothing, but in everything
by prayer and supplication,
with thanksgiving,
let your requests be made known to God;
and the peace of God,
which surpasses all understanding,
will guard your hearts and minds
through Christ Jesus."*
Philippians 4:6-7 (NKJV)

When I first walked through the "wilderness" of despair caused by severe, excruciating panic attacks and didn't see God answering my prayers quickly it was disheartening.

Is there a big difference between things we want and those we actually need? Our basic human needs have to be met: food, shelter, and love. There are other things we need that are important to us. What are they for different people? The list may be quite long and would vary from person to person. We may seek significance in our lives or opportunities for contribution. We also may do good and contribute, but the main motive being to seek significance. When we are honest with ourselves and God, we tell Him what we want and how we feel. God's perfect will is to give us everything that is good. Not everything that He gives us is what we want or what we ourselves consider good. Often, like a loving parent, He gives us what we need when we can't see the immediate benefit. If your loving parents were to give you a box of fresh broccoli with a gift card to a local health food store as a birthday gift, you most likely would be quite disappointed—what in the world were they thinking! May be a gym membership will be better for some of us, but not for everybody. Working out would require effort on our part and we don't see the positive results right away. It will take weeks and even months for visible changes to appear. We prefer to receive nice gifts we may use to our immediate satisfaction, not necessarily what is good for us.

I don't ever want to be phony with the Lord; I speak to Him openly, I cry and sometimes weep. There may be times when He is the only one who will listen. I believe that He is there, listening, even if I don't sense His presence. There are times when I need to emotionally hibernate and be alone. I don't want to spill the negativity out on my friends and family, nor dwell in self-pity. The spirit of deception has caused occasional self-loathing. I sometimes saw myself as a worthless case, and allowed misery a foothold in my soul.

In Matthew 7:7-11, we are to persevere in asking God: *"Ask, seek and knock…"* begging: "Lord, please…" not from entitlement, but from humility and, at times, in despair. I learned to *"come boldly before the throne of God,"* to *"pray without ceasing "* and to *"be constant in prayer."*

The most practical tip of all is to pray, pray, pray, which makes me regard myself *"according to the spirit",* enabling me to get my mind off myself.

Conversations with God: Prayer and Meditation

When you have difficult circumstances in life, do you ask God for wisdom and guidance, admitting you cannot possibly do it alone? Or are you like I was for so many years, waiting until you're at your wits end, trying to solve problems on your own, and only then remember the ultimate source of power, wisdom and peace?

I've heard that praying and meditating are two sides of the same coin we are to tithe to God. Prayer is speaking to God, and meditation is just dwelling in His presence and listening; meditating on words like love or on visions of heaven and God on the throne. Praying and meditating creates a dialog between me and my Creator.

❝ When I needed to sort things out, I spoke to my God...When my very soul was throbbing, I poured my heart out, asking God to relieve me from pain

Many people don't feel worthy even to pray to God for deliverance, but He longs for this relationship, that we would talk about everything on our hearts. When such a relationship is established, we can't help but be in awe of His power and might. As in any relationship, we need to learn to listen, not only talk about our needs and desires.

Being available to God, making an effort to spend time with Him and listening need to be a priority. At times (though not often enough), I pray with pen in hand and a notebook in front of me. Listening and writing down impressions on my heart has been eye-opening. I am not disappointed when I don't get a clear answer. I just write down what comes to mind. It is important to take notes in church too, because when the Lord speaks to me, it must be recorded.

It helps to write down verses on healing and read them often. I also thank God for my past healing and for the comfort He gives me.

When I feel down, I write lists of God's gifts to me and miracles He performed in my life as a reminder that I am loved and cherished by my Heavenly Father.

Meditating on the greatness of God when in distress made me shift my focus from me and my problems to Him and His greatness.

"What then shall we say? Is God unjust? Not at all! For he says to Moses, "I will have mercy on whom I have mercy, and I will have compassion on whom I have compassion." It does not, therefore, depend on man's desire or effort, but on God's mercy." Romans 9:14-16

God Answering Prayer

"God answers all prayers. Sometimes He says 'Yes', sometimes He says 'No', sometimes He says, 'You've got to be kidding!'" I love this saying and even have a mug with this very inscription as a reminder. Isn't it true for so many of us? Have you ever asked God for something and after receiving it, exclaimed in distress: "Oops!! I did not really mean it like that! This is too much to handle! Please take it baaaack!"?

How can we be sure that what we ask God for is good for us? I cannot possibly see the whole picture the way God sees it. What if that job I was begging God for requires long hours and puts a strain on my relationship with Him and with my family? What if the house I was dreaming and praying about (and finally got) requires too much maintenance and came with neighbors who drive me crazy? What if…

When I needed to sort things out, I spoke with my God. Some of the most heart-felt and in-depth talks I had with God had been during my half-hour long commuting through the mountains. Malibu, where I live, is a small town and I usually drive inland for shopping, work, or to run errands. In the canyon, radio and cell reception are very poor, bringing these distractions to a minimum. When my very soul was throbbing, I poured my heart out, asking God to relieve me from pain. I learned to cast my problems at the throne of my Heavenly Father. He could take care of all of them, in

His perfect timing. There is another saying about God answering prayers: He may say; "Yes," "Not yet," or "I have something better for you." At home, I read the Scriptures and devotionals, focusing on His goodness and healing. In church, I gave the Lord thanks through prayer and filled my heart with worship. This was my spiritual life in the midst of emotional crisis. I see now what I could have done differently, but I was growing, making small steps in my spiritual walk. I now begin my prayers with gratitude. But when it is not a habit yet, we have a tendency to cry for help first, and I was no exception…

I have many examples of answered prayer in my life. Years ago when I was living in Ukraine, a few months after I got saved, I found myself in a real turmoil. I was a single mother, sharing an apartment with my grandmother. My mother lived in the same city and visited us and helped almost daily. I was on a maternity leave from school I was working at, but due to the collapse of the Soviet economy, it was basically peanuts, barely enough to exist. My son was only a few months old and I was slowly regaining my strength. We needed the money, so I applied and was accepted to work at one of the first International schools in Kiev. I was very excited to get the job, which also was an answer to prayers. Then, only a couple of days before I was to start working, my grandmother and I got violently ill, unable to take care of the baby. At the same time, my mother ended up at the hospital. Our kind neighbors volunteered to take care of my child… I was truly desperate. I became a believer only a few months earlier and witnessed a few miracles already. This time I needed a big one. I was only learning about the power of prayer and fasting, but decided to give it a try. It was the first time when I fervently prayed while abstaining from food. Within three days, all turned around and we got well. I found a great doctor who helped my mother and I was at work, full of energy and with renewed belief in the power of prayer.

Since then, the Lord intervened a few times when I needed a job, for example, in Ukraine, when the first International school I worked at ceased to exist. By then, I completely trusted God in guiding me in all my decisions as I walked in faith. I was in the "spiritual bubble" so many newly saved people talk about. Many of my friends confirmed that they experienced firsthand the extra protection God reserves for "baby Christians" in order to strengthen their faith. I believe this to be true. It seemed as if the Lord gave me extra protection, extra favors, extra love, like we give to a newborn child. As I was maturing in my walk with Him, He withdrew somewhat, allowing me to gain strength, to make my own mistakes, but always watching me, being just a prayer away. This time, during my early walk with God, miracles were happening left and right. I would pray for a dream job at the new International school, then completely stop worrying and get the position within three days. I needed transportation to go to a relative's house in the country, with the baby and grandma. The parents of one of the students from International school heard of my ordeal and provided a car and driver, who took us to our destination and picked us up a month later, completely free of charge. I needed new clothes and they were given to me; I needed shoes and a colleague approached me with an envelope saying that the Lord told her to give me some money. I was on the receiving end of a flood of miracles. After experiencing this, I wonder how I drifted from the Lord's presence and dwelling in His mercy, but I did. There were times when I thought I lost this contact forever. I thought I made too many "mistakes," I've sinned too much to be forgiven. Thankfully, that was not the case. I was only beginning to learn about the nature of God. He mercifully accepted me and showed His love.

Years later, when I needed work in California I prayed and got my answer within three days again. One day in church, I had a clear thought about how much money we were to donate to a building fund. Our family could not afford to give away such a sum. There were bills to pay, groceries to buy… I was standing there in a pew, having a a silent dialog in my mind: "Lord, we can't afford to give this much…" "Get a job." "You know I looked around, I tried, there is nothing available." "Get a job." " But Lord, there is…" "Get a Job!" " Okay, if you say so, but…" "Get A Job!"

I went home and halfheartedly opened a classified section of a local newspaper (the Internet search was not popular yet). For months I looked almost every week in the Sunday classified section and there was nothing. To my surprise, there were two (!) ads from private Christian (!!) schools in the area, looking for math (!!!) teachers. I don't know why I was surprised—I was told to get a job. I sent my resume out the following day, had back-to-back interviews, and by the end of the week, had to decide at which school I shall be working, as I was accepted at both!

A different example of the power of prayer is the story of a friend. Jim was a Christian teacher and one day he caught himself looking with lust at one of the young girls he was ministering to. Realizing the power of temptation, he asked God to remove this desire, even if it meant using drastic methods. Within hours of that prayer, Jim developed a severe testicle infection that didn't go away for weeks! Wrenched with pain, he asked God to be cured and immediately was reminded that he got what he had asked for… the Lord did take away temptation by using very drastic measures, as requested.

Hindered Prayers

Throughout my life, over and over again, I asked myself if there is a chance I used up God's blessings. It was an immature question, I know, but for years I was stumbling in my faith, seeking wisdom and guidance, not knowing how to do it right.

I knew right from wrong, but time after time, I would try to keep my behavior in check, but inevitably slip. Being a human with a sinful nature is so frustrating at times! Things I would say or do when I was trying desperately to please others, to be liked, to fit in! All my intentions to please God in my actions were moved aside…Oh, Lord, thank you so much for being endlessly merciful! Thank you for promising not to give up on me if I don't give up. Thank you for being forgiving and merciful.

Keeping promises to God and God's Endless Mercies

I did not try to manipulate God with false promises, I had every intention to keep them, I really did, it just didn't always work out. So I would try to come up with what I thought would be a legitimate excuse. I was acting like daddy's little girl with her loving father. I knew that He loved me and I was hoping to avoid punishment. How ignorant! I'm so grateful I'm still alive—seriously! The Lord didn't allow Moses to enter the Promised Land because he did not follow God's instruction to the "t" when asking God to provide water for the Israelites, thus showing disrespect rather than complete trust in the Creator of all. God's instruction to Moses was clear: speak to the rock and the water will flow from it. Instead, Moses struck the rock twice, causing the water to flow to the satisfaction of thirsty Israelites. Not a big deal, right? Not to God! Moses showed disbelief in God's promise and word and did not honor Him as holy before the people.

" The Lord has His perfect timing. Don't be discouraged.

On the other hand, the Lord forgave David for his affair with Bathsheba and the murder of her husband to cover up her pregnancy. David's genuine repentance and love for God was so earnest and deep that God called him "a man after God's own heart." The Bible has examples of forgiveness of sins, and punishment for what at first seems like misbehavior. His ways are truly unbeknown to men.

There is endless grace when I do my part, walking in faith. When I go my own way, I suffer the consequences of those choices, not as a punishment from God, but as a result of my lack of good judgment.

Once I was in a Community Bible Study where we studied the Book of Daniel. I was influenced by a story about Daniel and his friends' refusal to eat delicacies from the king's table in Babylonian captivity, instead, taking vegetables and water. I decided to do my own spin on fasting and to resist shopping for a few months. I shared it with my group at the Bible Study as well as a few of my girlfriends, waving my flag of righteousness left and right. Resisting the shopping felt totally right and manageable, but it got harder and harder. After a few weeks I slipped. I was quite inventive in coming up with a legitimate excuse for buying something I "needed." It was like a strong force pulling me towards the store, luring me in. So I slipped again. As a result, I was guilty and ashamed of my lack of willpower. I imagined the Accuser pointing at me, saying: "You see, you see! You failed! You are such a loser!"

My intentions were good, but my will was weak. Yes, it was not the only time when I would promise something to God as a sacrifice, but keep it only for a while. Was it because my "fasts" were not biblical? Was it because of my lack of willpower, or the essence of human nature? Was it because I was relying on my willpower instead of the power of God? Did I try to prove something to the One who created me and knows all about me? I was trying to please God by my acts and it can't be wrong, right? I am supposed to do what is pleasing to God, so why is it that *"I do not do the good I want, but the evil I do not want is what I keep on doing."* (Romans 7:19) *"I don't really understand myself, for I want to do what is right, but I don't do it. Instead, I do what I hate… I don't want to do what is wrong, but I do it anyway… it is sin living in me that does it."* (Romans 7:15-20, NLT) This quote is from the letter written by the Apostle Paul! Realizing that even Paul was battling the same issues that I face comforts me is the sense that I am not alone in this struggle. I do need to repent of my wrongdoing, for sure. But I need not dwell in misery of failure. I am to get up, learn my lesson and move forward, asking for strength and wisdom to do better next time. My behavior is not perfect. "The spirit is willing, but the flesh is weak." (Matthew 26:41.) Thankfully, God is not after perfection in us, as we can't attain it.

My heart delights to be with Him, and I strive to please Him with my actions. I am learning to check my actions and words:

would they please my Lord? When I ask this question daily, my actions follow. I love reading the encouraging verses in the Bible that help me not to give up even when I feel weary or like a total failure. *"And let us not grow weary of doing good, for in due season we will reap, if we do not give up."(Galatians 6:9, ESV)*

Thank you, Father, for giving me the strength I need to run this race called life. "Show me your ways, Lord, teach me your paths. Guide me in your truth and teach me, for you are God my Savior, and my hope is in you all day long." (Psalm 25:4-5)

Collective and Intercessory Prayer

It is also called corporate prayer, but I personally don't like this expression, as it sounds too business-like. Regardless what you call it, there is something very special about friends and even strangers praying together, joining in faith, to overcome challenges in life. It is very encouraging to know my troubles and concerns are being lifted up to heaven by friends and sometimes by people I don't even know. I received letters from my students who revealed that they were praying for my healing, which was so uplifting! I will never know how many more people prayed for my healing, but I know they did. Why was I not healed on thea spot after so many people lifted me up in prayer? It is only for my Creator to know. I was comforted in many ways and came out stronger. I learned to trust God. You don't want to be disappointed when prayer doesn't seem to work. The Lord is a healer, yet it is hard to comprehend the reasons behind healing or not being healed—there is no black and white. It is great when you can say after you went through pain "I'm glad I went through this."

The Lord has His perfect timing. Don't be discouraged.

Fasting

It is good for me to go on a fast from time to time. The most common kind of fasting is sustaining from food for a certain period of time. I can go a day with just drinking water, but there were times when after a half-day without food, I became dizzy and had to stop. There can be a physiological explanation: toxin build-up in the system or lack of certain nutrients. Only healthy people should go without food for prolonged periods of time. I need to be very careful and consult a doctor if I want to go on a strict fast. There are other ways to fast and things I can avoid as a willing sacrifice. A list of unnecessary things I try to "fast from" include the Internet, chocolate, other "choice food." As I am writing this I have not been on social media in over a month— can you imagine? When I have to check my e-mail, I do it fast and try to log off. It is so easy to get distracted when online! Hours could pass before I pull myself out of virtual reality, which is addictive.

The whole idea of giving up something is not to diet or "cleanse." When I stop doing something I like or go without eating, I remember with each moment of deprivation why I am constraining myself and give praise to God. It opens a different way of communication. When we talk about "sacrifices of praise," it has to mean something. How often do we sacrifice anything to praise The One and Only, The Alpha And Omega, The Creator of it all? Fasting helps me to keep it in perspective. When I learned about fasting, I used it only when I desperately needed something. It was something like: "Lord, you see what a good girl I am, sacrificing this thing for you. Can you please reward me for being good and grant this wish/request?" How childish, I know, but we often use prayer in the same way—asking for things. Even if we do pray regularly, how much time do we spend praising God and how quickly do we switch to uttering our shopping lists of requests? I am learning to fast as a means of getting in the right mindset and to put my priorities in order, God and my relationship with Him being number one.

CHAPTER FIFTEEN

Lessons in Stillness

"Be still, and know that I am God.
I will be exalted among the nations,
I will be exalted in the earth!"
Psalm 46:10 ESV

Solitude and Affliction

I need solitude on occasion to seek answers to troubling questions. Sometimes I need "me" time to replenish my busy life with beauty and rest. I welcome this kind of isolation.

Depression and anxiety caused a forced, deep seclusion and emotionally throbbing loneliness. Like so many others in this condition, I initially disconnected from life and people. I even developed agoraphobia: becoming fearful of crowds and public places. Thankfully, it was short-term. Prolonged bouts of solitude were strange and frightening, contradicting my outgoing nature. I longed to be myself, back in the swing of things—fun-loving and social. For a while, this cloud of desperation was covering the horizon and there seemed to be no escape. I was frightened and at a loss. The worst yet was a feeling of being disconnected from the core of my being, disconnected from God.

The Challenge of Being Still

When I'm ill, I am reduced to just being and not doing. Why do I often see it as a negative? I don't always have to be on the run; there are times when I need to slow down, reflect and just be, enjoying the present moment, not reliving the past or peeking into the future. Mostly, it's hard to clear my head, as there is always something to distract me from taking a well-deserved break.

We've heard that patience is a skill to be mastered. For many of us, it is quite a challenging task. For an active person to do nothing but reflect, waiting on the voice of God and learning to be still seemed difficult but proved to be possible. Many of us know the phrase, be a human being, not a human doing, but I was conditioned to "do," not just "be." When Jesus walked on earth, He explained to Martha why He preferred Mary's attitude. It is important to put food on the table, but moments of simple faith and stillness at Jesus' feet are better than a feast. This story reminds me to keep my priorities in check: when I can spend time with the God of all creation, let the dirty dishes pile up for a while. If I try to do all the chores first, I may be too tired later to "sit and listen at the Lord's feet"—whatever that may imply today: attending a Bible study, reading a devotional, watching good teaching on YouTube or spending time in prayer and meditation.

Slowing Down

Addressing my health issue forced me to take drastic measures in self-care. It may not sound scriptural for some, as we are trained to be servants on behalf of our Lord. It is correct that we need to show hospitality and to love and care for others, but we also need time to rejuvenate and be filled. If all we do is pour out into others, pretty soon we may try to run on empty, wondering why we can't move.

One of the most beautiful and beloved Psalms begins with the words: *"The Lord is my shepherd; I shall not want. He makes me lie down in green pastures. He leads me beside still waters. He restores my soul." (Psalm 23:1-3, ESV)* It never registered before: "He makes me lie down"! My God knows that I need rest and at times He will make me take time to rest if I forget or think it unimportant.

I need to remember to slow down, take a break, look around, go outside and just observe nature. Breathe, slowly and fully. Even in the busy schedule of a high school math instructor, I found time for simple pleasures. On occasion, my colleagues and I took our lunch outside instead of eating at our desks. I graded papers by the lake or in front of the picture window with a nice view. I worked on my computer in beautiful park settings. I made the simple commitment to leave my usual environment often. I often post on social media my "office location for the day" with beautiful scenery, and I hope to encourage my friends to do the same when possible.

Running a good race, as mentioned by the Apostle Paul, is important. But at times we are forced to take detours in the wilderness or stop for reflection and be filled on a mountaintop or in a valley. Such a task is tough for overly active individuals. Being a habitual overachiever, it was quite challenging for me to learn to let things go with my typically fast-paced life. I learned this lesson during difficult times when I was stricken by pain, sorrow and despair. I prayed for pain to depart so that I could gain control over my life.

Throughout my life I was not always disciplined with my quiet time with God. When I was busy I did not always allot time to read the Bible, reflect and pray at appointed times. I did not make time for any Bible studies or prayer and fellowship with other believers. When I had to go on disability, all of a sudden I had a lot of free time and got into a habit of reading the Bible and devotions regularly. I was once again seeking God and being drawn closer to Him. This time I had all the time to focus on this task, as if it was orchestrated for that particular purpose.

Lying in bed one day, at my wits end from suffering in pain and immobility, the Lord spoke to me. On that particular day, both the Bible and devotional book I was reading had words about stillness and patience. Shortly after reading, the phone rang. It was my dear friend from work, Nancy. She said: "I was thinking about you this morning. I don't know why, but I believe the Lord impressed on my heart to read you this passage on stillness." I was beginning to get the message. When an hour or so later a pastor called and repeated the same Bible passage with the word "stillness," I smiled. *"Be still, and know that I am God." (Psalm 46:10, ESV)*

These were the words repeated to me again and again. It was as if my Heavenly Father sent me a gentle encouragement: "You are not alone, my child, I am in control; hold on." I was learning the importance of being still. God has amazing ways to prove His point.

This message about stillness was so powerful that it influenced me for years to come. It was planted in my heart, took root and grew. This stillness before the Lord needs to be watered with His Word and fertilized by prayer.

Patience and Waiting on God

"And so after waiting patiently, Abraham received what was promised (by God)" (Hebrews 6:15)

I have to admit that patience was not my virtue of choice. Like everyone else, I like instant gratification. Would you like instant answer to your prayers? For many years, drive-through prayer life was totally my thing! In these times, who has patience to wait? When suddenly—BAM! I was unable to move for days at a time— no more running around and multitasking. I learned to wait and to be grateful in the process.

Now I enjoy being active again, but often I remind myself to slow down, not to say "yes" to every request coming my way. I am more mindful to stop and ask God what He wants me to do and how I am to arrange my schedule.

In his writings, Apostle Paul mentioned a "thorn in the flesh" from which he suffered. The Lord could have easily healed him by removing this affliction, but He didn't. Instead, He told him My grace is sufficient. This "thorn in the flesh" sounds very much like my panic attacks. At its worst, a panic attack feels like a stab to your chest. It comes without warning. Weeks, months, or even years can pass without one, then suddenly, out of nowhere, it strikes. I learned to live with the possibility of sudden relapses, but I am not afraid anymore. I even grew to find benefits in going through this experience. It taught me to be still and reinforced the idea that patience is a virtue.

Dying To Self

When the name of the game is impatience and overachievement, it is a huge challenge to believe in God's perfect timing. *"Be still before the Lord and wait patiently for Him..." (Psalm 37:7)*

As a long-time gardener, I know well that in order for a seed to be transformed into a plant that will yield either gorgeous flowers or delicious vegetables, that seed needs to go through a germination process. After being harvested, a seed needs to stay dormant to be prepared for the next planting season. Placed underground. it needs to stay there for a while. I could not speed up the growing process, but I can make sure to add good soil, fertilizer and water. But just by my sheer will, a seed will not produce a juicy tomato in one day. It takes time.

Another gardening example is that of a grapevine, which produces the sweetest fruit under harsh and extreme weather conditions, in soil seemingly unsuitable for such plants to grow. Grapevines also need to be pruned back to the vine to produce fruit the following year, lying dormant for the winter season. From a human perspective, who wants to be "pruned" to "bear fruit"? But that is exactly what many of us have to go through, as painful as it seems, in a moment when all "unnecessary" things are being cut off from our lives.

Now I know from experience that it is indeed possible to train myself to be still. I don't know how I would've gotten through this without dwelling in God's presence. The Lord used this time to get through to me. The main thing I worked on was learning to be still. The next step was putting my pride and selfishness on His altar as a sacrifice.

In our self-centered culture, it is foreign to have a spirit of submission and lowliness. It is all about "me." Although there is some focus on teamwork in the workplace, it is nothing compared to the selfishness and walk-over-bodies-to-get-it attitude. Everyone has ego imbedded in him or her. The fall of humanity began with Adam and Eve being tempted by the prospect of being like God. The fall of Lucifer was also caused by his desire to be like God:

"How you are fallen from heaven, O shining star, son of the morning! You have been thrown down to the earth, you who destroyed the nations of the world. For you said to yourself, 'I will ascend to heaven and set my throne above God's stars. I will preside on the mountain of the gods far away in the north. I will climb to the highest heavens and be like the Most High.'" (Isaiah 14:12-14, NLT) He was craving power and glory, as are many people in our culture. The desire to be like God is not always evident, but in some self-improvement books, of which I read many, there is a twisting of scripture, that we are made in the image of God, so we have unlimited power. But God is the only omnipotent one and we should revere Him, not considering ourselves to be His equal. God created us for His purpose. I don't want to ever forget who the boss is here! Yes, I am a daughter of the Almighty, created in His image, and with faith I can move mountains, but it's not faith in my own power that does it, but faith in His power in me. I can do nothing without His strength—nada!

Thanksgiving and Humility

One of the big lessons throughout the ordeal of "disorder" was learning and exercising humility. I once thought of myself as Superwoman. I was giving some credit to God, but not truly giving him all the glory for being delivered from illness or other difficulties.

The story of Jesus healing the ten lepers comes to mind. These people were suffering all their lives from pain and shame, being social outcasts. Then one beautiful day they were miraculously healed. They left rejoicing, and then one came running back to thank Jesus for His miracle of healing. One out of ten! Sometimes I wonder if only ten percent of those who are healed nowadays worship God in awe and gratitude. How is your prayer life? Does it resound with thanksgiving? Let's continue to learn the benefit of and apply prayers of gratitude throughout the day.

"Humble yourselves, therefore, under God's mighty hand, that He may lift you up in due time. Cast all your anxiety on Him because He cares for you." (1 Peter 5:6-7)

I need to daily remind myself to get my mind off of me, or else the ego runs rampant! I must focus on what I am grateful for in my life. I am learning to do a brain scan for ungodly thoughts and words. Forget peer pressure! I should be much more mindful about my actions when I fully realize that God is aware of my every thought and action!

At times I got upset with God's decisions, acting like a spoiled child who had come to expect more and more miracles in her life out of entitlement, as if I was "a favorite child." At the beginning, when I first became a Christian, the Lord answered many prayers quickly—thus I became accustomed to having good things happen. But He did that in the beginning to help my faith grow; then I was expected to walk after having "crawled" in this journey of faith.

CHAPTER SIXTEEN

Spirit R Us

"Be strong and courageous.
do not be afraid; do not be discouraged,
for the Lord your God will be with you
wherever you go."
Joshua 1:9

God as a Loving Father

If you have children, you know that they are pretty selfish by nature. They demand and fuss if things don't go their way. They need to be taught and guided to learn the proper behavior. Does a parent meet all her children's capricious requests all the time? What kind of person will my son become if I only give in without giving him the most valuable thing—a chance to grow, achieve and overcome obstacles on his own? I admit, watching a child make mistakes hurts. But I can't live his life for him, nor would I know how. I need to pray for him and teach him to ask God for guidance and seek the counsel of godly elders. Of course, when my child was little, I would jump up at the first sound of his cry, ready to make everything better instantly. But nurturing a small child and guiding a young adult is different. I had to move from the hands-on parent to an active observer.

This is the kind of parenting we also receive from our Heavenly Father. He observes our potential for love as well as rebellion and other things He knows we are capable of, He sometimes intervenes and is always ready to give His perfect counsel. When He disciplines us, He does it as a loving parent, as a good father disciplines his offspring to train them in righteousness. Our Creator focuses on building our character rather than meeting all our demands.

❝ *Our Creator focuses on building our character, not necessarily meeting all our demands*

As a new believer, I lived insulated in a "spiritual bubble," having most of my infantile demands met, prayers often answered fast, many within three days. I learned to say "thank you" but was not learning patience just yet. My intuition tells me that I was delivered for such a time as this... and that there is a strong force that does not want me to live a transformed life, dwelling in God's glory. This force is trying very hard to lead me away from unity with God. It is trying to lead me away from my first love, the love I felt when I was first saved. But I shall not fret, knowing that God is in charge. One of the resources always available to me is prayer. When everything seems to be spinning out of control and my carefully planned life is falling apart, my loving Heavenly Father is just a prayer away. Even if in the midst of emotional turmoil I don't feel His presence, I shall rest assured He is listening. When I am at a total loss as to what to do, I can rest on His promises, all of which are listed in the Bible. I can meditate on these promises and utter prayers, anytime, anywhere.

The enemy comes to kill, steal and destroy and in his craftiness, he will gladly throw us into despair. He wants to rob us of our joy and faith, to shake our very trust in God. When we are grieving, many of us can doubt God and His will. Don't you think that such a mindset in us makes the enemy quite happy? With the possibilities of a generational curse, in a world where spiritual battles are taking place daily, being on guard and prepared is crucial. There is no room for laziness on the battlefield—you may get killed! *"Whom have I in heaven but You? And there is none upon earth that I desire besides You. My flesh and my heart fail; but God is the strength of my heart and my portion forever." (Psalm 73:25-26, NKJV).*

We are given authority to speak to the evil spirits and to cast them out in the name of Jesus. The Lord's Prayer is given to us in Mark 9 and it is powerful. On numerous occasions I prayed it over and over again; spiritual mayhem subsided and left. The Bible is full of examples of evil spirits possessing people. I questioned if I was one of these possessed individuals. What if all that was happening to me was a result of spiritual warfare? Did I open a door to it somehow by my evil deeds and sinful actions?

I went through a "spiritual checkup": What are my unconfessed sins? Do I gossip? Do I harbor unforgiveness and resentment? Do I covet something too much? Do I keep my God first or did I put something else on a pedestal in my life? It is good to run such a check-up to keep myself aligned with the will of God. After that I put on the armor of God to withstand spiritual battles, as it is crucial to be well-equipped for them. This armor is listed in the New Testament: *"Finally, be strong in the Lord and in the strength of his might. Put on the whole armor of God, that you may be able to stand against the schemes of the devil. For we do not wrestle against flesh and blood, but against the rulers, against the authorities, against the cosmic powers over this present darkness, against the spiritual forces of evil in the heavenly places. Therefore take up the whole armor of God, that you may be able to withstand in the evil day, and having done all, to stand firm. Stand therefore, having fastened on the belt of truth, and having put on the breastplate of righteousness, and, as shoes for your feet, having put on the readiness given by the gospel of peace. In all circumstances take up the shield of faith, with which you can extinguish all the flaming darts of the evil one; and take the helmet of salvation, and the sword of the Spirit, which is the word of God, praying at all times in the Spirit, with all prayer and supplication." (Ephesians 6:10-18, ESV)*

So here is a shortened list: a belt of truth, breastplate of righteousness, shoes of the gospel of peace, shield of faith, helmet of salvation, and the sword of the Spirit, which is the word of God. All are important, but I would like to point out the last words: this spiritual armor needs to be supplemented with constant prayer.

Memorizing Scriptures

Confronting the enemy with the truth and promises of God's Word makes a lot of difference—if only I did it every time! Unfortunately, I was not introduced to this godly way of living early on and still have a lot of catching up to do. In preparing for life's battles, I need to remind myself that there is strength in weakness. I admit my limitations. I can't fight all on my own; I need God on my side. His Word is encouraging in various life situations. I look up verses relevant to a current challenge and speak them out loud, as God's word is powerful and active. Speaking scriptures out loud and memorizing verses is a great and powerful tool.

I prayed for my healing and meditated on it. Why don't I do it all the time? The spirit is willing but the flesh (including my memory) is weak. I tried to recall the verses but realized that something weird was happening with my memory—it was all but gone. Forget memorizing verses, often I am lucky to recall a word or a name during a conversation! When I want to memorize a Bible verse, my brain freezes. In the past, I would have memorized a couple of pages in an hour.

In school, I had to memorize pages of poetry and prose, theorems, historical facts and dates. I still can recite the longest texts I committed to memory then. I wish I knew the same amount of Bible verses. Nowadays it takes a lot of effort to memorize a line; anyone with me? We forget objects, places, and, worst of all, occasionally we forget the name of a close friend when trying to introduce her to others! Currently this memorization process is an on-going challenge and it is going in spurts. My mind does not always seem to work as it used to, but should I use it as an excuse to give up? When I asked myself this question, I rose to the challenge. After all, I can regularly commit to memory new words and phrases in the language that is foreign to me. Often it happens without my trying. I remember sentences, though I cannot always recall where I heard or read them. How else can I be writing this? So I am positive that with persistence and repetition, I can memorize and be able to recite encouraging verses from the Bible. It proved to be especially useful when I am awakened in the middle of the night. Speaking words from memory when I am just lying in bed in the dark is a powerful way to keep destructive thoughts from becoming overpowering. When I am going through spiritual battles, reciting God's word keeps the enemy at bay and gives me relief and comfort in times of trouble.

One of my favorite verses is a promise that He will finish the good work He has begun in me.

God's Word

God's Word is a part of the spiritual armor I need.

I don't ever want to be legalistic about reading my Bible. When I start a Bible reading plan in January, I have every intention to follow through, but what are my motives? Do I want to impress others by saying how many times I have read the Bible in its entirety? Do I want to appear spiritual and earn "brownie points" with men and God (in that order) or do I really hunger for wisdom and insight I gain from studying it?

Spiritual Medication: Meditating on Healing

Healing usually takes time, and it helps to meditate on the Word of God while I am waiting. The word used in the Bible for "meditate" is the same as the word that describes a cow chewing on its cud. The process is quite slow: chewing, swallowing, digesting, eliminating, and chewing again, through all four of the cow's four stomachs! Sounds unpleasant, even disgusting—especially for city dwellers removed from farming. But in ancient times many knew about this process, as many had farm animals, and it describes the very slow process of digestion, encouraging us to return to God's word again and again.

I apply healing scriptures as I would a prescribed remedy, with no side effects!

"Lord, my God, I called to you for help, and You healed me"
(Psalm 30:2)

"Worship the Lord your God, and his blessings will be on your food and water. I will take away sickness from among you." (Exodus 23:25)

"Praise the Lord, O my soul, and forget not all His benefits, Who forgives all your sins and heals all your diseases, Who redeems your life from the pit and crowns you with love and compassion." (Psalm 103:2-4)

Based on these Psalms, there is a conditional statement: *if* we worship and praise God, *then* He heals us. I claim the promises of healing in my life as a child of God, but I must remember: a condition to healing is praise and worship.

How should I worship? What does it truly mean to offer sacrifices of praise? Does it mean that I should worship even when I don't feel grateful, but choose to override my complaining and murmuring heart? Giving the sacrifice of praise in all circumstances had to become a discipline for me. In times of trials, I wanted to throw in the towel; rejoicing was the last thing on my mind. I didn't feel it, but I learned not to indulge my emotions, nor bow down to them.

Sing it When You Mean it, or Maybe I've asked for It?

What we say always has a meaning. It is true in all aspects of our lives. What we say in the presence of God is even more imperative, even if we don't carefully consider everything we say in prayer or sing in worship. We may ask for something without thinking through possible consequences and then wonder about the sudden trials and challenges we face. Remember, as God is listening to our prayers, He may say "yes," "no"' or "you must be kidding!" and then grant it nevertheless…

It is right to ask your Creator to bring you closer to Him, to purify your heart with a cleansing fire, when you're sincere. But I am too much of a chicken to deliberately ask for pain. I am scared to do that because I know that God is listening and He can give me exactly what I am asking for. When I was suffering, I wondered if I brought it on myself by wrongdoing or my idle words. The pain I experienced reminded me of being refined by fire, the process used to purify gold or silver from ore.

I love worship songs and I like to sing along to them in church or in my car. When I can deeply relate to lyrics in some way, these songs become so much more meaningful. On occasion a song will be sung that I cannot relate to. They are beautiful worship songs, but I can't sing the words I don't mean. At times there are lyrics about God stirring fire in a person's soul or putting a soul on fire. There are different fires to talk about: refining fire that burns away all the impurities in a sinful nature of humans and a bright burning fire of passion towards God. They are beautiful worship songs but some verses about fire I choose not to sing nowadays—maybe not yet. I remember too well how the fire in my soul felt like… I feel as I was refined by fire already and I am not ready to voluntarily invite it back, thank you very much! Call me weak but I don't want to experience it again. I do want to get closer to my God and follow His will wherever I go, but I hope not to go through too much pain and suffering if possible. Yes, I know, I am such a sissy… I ask God to be gentle when He is guiding me. On occasion during worship in church I make up my own words, giving God praise and expressing my love.

Just the other day I was singing in church when I stumbled upon the words about the Lord breaking a man's heart and cleansing him. I was not ready to sing these words, so I sang what came into my heart. I also was quietly praying for strength and wisdom.

Do you ever ask God to purify your soul when you pray or worship? Do you ever sing in church just following the worship leader, not meaning the words, your mind drifting to other things? Recently I was watching a video on the Internet, where a speaker asked a man in the audience to sing Amazing Grace. He responded by beautifully singing this song accapella. The speaker then asked this singer to envision that his brother just got out of jail, his life totally turned around and restored, to imagine that all the storms in life were just calmed down by the power of God. Than he asked the singer to sing the song again. If the first performance was beautiful the second was powerful; there was a huge difference in the emotion and the range of singing—it was totally breathtaking and empowering! We need to mean it when we sing, fully pouring our hearts out to the One who gave us this life,

Words have power

Referring to the beginning of creation John 1:1 states: *"In the beginning was the Word, and the Word was with God, and the Word was God." God inspired words* in the Bible and it is powerful. In a sense, so are the words we speak to each other. Words have power to hurt or to uplift, comfort and inspire. When we hear an inspiring message, our bodies are flooded with endorphins and neurotransmitters that increase the level of serotonin and make us feel good physically and emotionally.

A few years ago, I was reading a book by Debbie Macomber in which she described gathering with a group of women for years. These friends encouraged and uplifted each other. Around the New Year each lady would choose a word to ponder for the year to come. I thought it was such a good idea. I liked it so much I didn't want to wait till January. It was still September; the Day of Atonement and Yom Kippur were approaching—a New Year as well. I prayed for the word to be given to me. As an answer, I got not one but two: persistence and perseverance. What was that about? I slowly realized that I needed to persist in completing what God told me to do, to encourage others by writing this book. I was moving forward, but the constant reminder of past pain caused me to retreat to recuperate. At times I wanted to give up as the physical and emotional pain of revisiting agonizing memories was so real, so raw... still, I knew I wasn't to choose another word until these two were fully manifested in my life.

Words do have significance; they can inspire or hurt us. "Sticks and stones can break my bones, but words will never hurt me" is only true when we give those words different meaning, otherwise it may bother a person deeply, causing fear and anxiety. When someone was emotionally bullied and called names as a child, it is likely to haunt him or her for years to come. Also, when we say: I am not talented, I am not worthy, I am not smart—those ideas stick. As a result, we don't see ourselves as the Crown of God's Creation, His Masterpiece.

I didn't want to give any power to negative words any longer. It became important for me to learn to use the right words, even to describe my condition and symptoms. The expression "panic attack" sounded too extreme; it seemed to hold certain power. In my self-talk, I resolved not to use it anymore so that the phrase didn't have such a grip on me. It was a bit more challenging not to use it when describing to others what was happening to me, but I tried to explain it by using words like "annoyance," "episode," "state." Unfortunately, when writing this book, I needed to be more specific and using powerful negative words produced painful setbacks for me.

Tuned in to God's Presence

How about getting into the habit of repenting, of saying: "I am sorry" to our Heavenly Father? How persistent am I in dwelling in God's Word and presence? I was encouraged by Daniel's example of praying three times a day on my knees and try to follow it as much as I can. Praying like that in gratitude and worship creates a special closeness with my Creator. Speaking to God out loud, in prayer and worship really makes a difference in my spiritual growth. What a beautiful relationship I am developing with My God when I am committed and persistent in my effort to take time to establish this bond.

It takes about ten weeks of consistent repetition to create a lasting change and form a habit. It is not always easy to establish a new practice on the first try. It does take time and effort to let go of the old ways and replace them with new habits. We have to break the old ways we are so accustomed to and get on with a new; it is a slow process on many occasions. Often something comes up, "life happens," challenges occur. There always can be one excuse or the other. We get caught up in things and drift away from committing to doing what is crucial. We do take showers quite often, don't we? Why then do we still neglect to worship our God at appointed times daily and read His word? This must be the reason why we waver between living as a carnal and a spiritual person.

I need to persevere if I want to create lasting positive change for years to come. I witnessed firsthand how God works in my life when I spend time every day in prayer, meditation, worship and Bible reading. Nowadays I am also getting in the habit of asking myself a question: am I pleasing God with my actions and words I speak? Am I honoring my Father? With effort and persistence, this too will become a daily pattern of thinking.

Courage

"Be strong and courageous!" is one of my favorite commands from the Bible. These words are mentioned many times, especially in the Old Testament. Time and time again, God promised to give strength to those who believe and follow His commands. There are numerous passages in the Bible that are very encouraging in times of stress and doubt. God called his people to action on so

many occasions and He provided guidance, encouragement and protection. I felt encouraged to be proactive on my path to healing.

In John 5:1-7 there is a story of a disabled man who was lying by the pool of healing waters. The water had these healing properties but not all the time…only on special occasions when *"an Angel of God will stir it."* At such times, only the person who got to the water first was healed. Can you imagine the competition? One needed to be trained for Special Olympics to outrun the others.

When Jesus asked this particular disabled man if he wanted to be well, the man's response was that there was no one to get him into the water on time. Jesus, feeling compassion, commanded him to take up his mat and walk. So he did, completely cured. In order to be healed, this man had to do something, to act. There were two ways: to get to the water first or to obey God's word spoken by Jesus. Both ways required action. This story teaches us to take action on our healing, as well as in our lives in general. We need to obey God's word and His commands.

Unfortunately, not everyone who is sick will get well and not every paraplegic will walk again. But those who are disabled hopefully will find a calling and meaning to their lives in Christ. Once again, Joni Ericson Tada comes to mind, a courageous woman who found strength in God after a diving accident left her "disabled" almost five decades ago. God made her very able and she is helping thousands upon thousands to find strength through belief in God, support groups as well as helping and encouraging others. Her ministry, Joni And Friends, an International Disability Center, reaches to people and churches around the world through radio, television, books and the Internet to raise disability awareness and help those in dire need of wheelchairs, compassion and realization of God's love, even in this fallen world full of grief and pain.

As I think about participants in Special Olympics today, I admire these people. They do not give up, sulking about their disabilities, as painful and devastating as they are. Through unimaginable pain, they challenge themselves, moving forward and inspiring everyone who sees them.

Many stressful situations in life are inevitable. Withstanding them with least damage to our spiritual connection and mental health is the key. It's not about if we ever get knocked down, it's what we will do to try to get up and eventually thrive. God must have His way in us: His goal is to mold us into the kind of person He intends us to become, using whatever means He sees fit.

CHAPTER SEVENTEEN

Drenched in Light

"For I know the plans I have for you," declares The Lord,
"plans to prosper you and not to harm you,
plans to give you hope and a future."
Jeremiah 29:1

Rocks

The pathway to healing leaves clues. Remember the story of Hansel and Gretel? Their wicked stepmother despised them so much that she charged her husband to lead the two small children to a forest and to leave them there. If these kids had collected rocks and thrown them on the ground instead of breadcrumbs, they would've been able to follow them later and find the way back home. When we are in trouble and use something that works, we can later retrieve these methods and use them again—we can follow the same path. We can use our "rocks" to lead us back to wellbeing. Have you ever seen rocks with inscriptions? I really like ones with the Fruit of the Spirit carved or painted onto them: Love, Joy, Peace, Patience, Kindness, Goodness, Faithfulness, Gentleness and Self-Control. These are also my rocks to lead me back to being centered on the ultimate Rock of our Salvation.

How many times did I go to a women's retreat and hear again and again the stories of deliverance from pain and suffering, sometimes unimaginable? Those experiences made me wonder: how resilient can we be? How much strength can God give us?

God does not promise to deliver us from every misfortune that comes our way. As a matter of fact, we are basically guaranteed to face trials. Thankfully, by seeking his council we will be equipped to withstand such trials: *"…count it all joy when you fall into various trials, knowing that the testing of your faith produces patience. But let patience have its perfect work, that you may be perfect and complete, lacking nothing."* (James 1:2-4, NKJV)

Everyday tasks and duties are pulling our attention away from centering on God. Many times I had my priorities twisted, even though I thought I was doing things in proper order. For some reason, my most meaningful relationships with God and family seemed not as important as work, errands and activities. I had no time for prayer or deep conversations with the ones I love. As a result, I grew frustrated and angry instead of growing in love. Mismanaging priorities led to aggravation, annoyance and disappointment. There was definitely something wrong with this picture—I needed to put first things first.

Do we need to repent of our fears? Maybe. I've heard that faith and fear cannot coexist. They are mutually exclusive.

God sends me divine appointments or flat out miracles to encourage me and to show me His love. I remind myself to display God's love wherever I go.

I like putting puzzles together. It is an addiction of sort, because once I start, I need to finish. I am okay with half-finished projects collecting dust around the house, but not puzzles. They have to be finished. When my back begins to hurt, I get up but still walk around the table like a hawk, looking for stray pieces. What if everything that caused anxiety in my life was a puzzle that needed to be sorted out and put together? I know the picture is somewhere, but I'm not able to see it yet. Though I longed to see its beauty, it was yet to emerge, known only to The Creator.

Setbacks

I never want to experience an "episode" again. I am committed to finding ways to be rid of them once and for all. I'll do anything to be free forever from the familiar symptoms of intense anxiety. Over a few years they diminished significantly, without permanent use of medication, but by using therapies and techniques that I had accumulated in my "tool box." The more I practiced awareness of potential triggers, the better care I took of my overall health; thus, the recurrence was seldom.

It is very unfortunate, but anxiety symptoms do return on occasion. In the beginning, when I finally began to feel better, I didn't expect setbacks. I was overwhelmed with joy when, for the first time, I was symptom-free for a whole week. I thought I was completely cured. Imagine my devastation when it came back! It was difficult to accept, but setbacks will come. At first they occurred more often, then months could pass before I experienced the dreaded symptoms. It took a while to be prepared and not be afraid or devastated. Now I play my own psychologist and guide; I look for what could possibly cause this setback, how can I prevent it in the future, and what am I to do if I begin to feel anxious.

Maintenance

I began recognizing events that were likely to trigger a downward spiral and to assign different meaning to things I was unable to avoid or control. With vigilance I can avoid the accumulation of anxiety that may develop into an out-of-control tailspin. It's much easier to prevent it before it becomes a full-blown episode.

You would think that by now, after years of researching anxiety, I would be way ahead of this game. I am, but the sneaky thing keeps resurfacing! It can manifest in my body as the weirdest pains and aches. Chest pain, back pain, stomach cramps, or shoulder tension—they come back as a result of fear that sneaks in. Sometimes it creeps in without my knowledge, but because I am familiar with the symptoms, I am able to retrace my emotional conflict to the origin. I also have a list of quick remedies, first being deep breathing. I had to compile this "instant fix" list to keep close by, because I have a tendency to forget some of the things without frequent use. My mental checklist: breathe, refocus, laugh, pray, meditate, etc. At times I had to use whatever I could recall in the moment.

> ❝ **Staying in constant gratitude and conscientiously choosing joy became my anchors in life**

The best way is prevention, so if I work out at least three times a week (preferably every day) and eat a clean nutritious diet, I am more likely to ward off relapses. Being sidetracked or sick, not working out or spending quiet time in prayer and meditation is when I am susceptible to a dreaded relapse. Though episodes still occur on occasion, thankfully they became less frequent and intense. I am back to living a full, productive, joyous life. Thank you, Lord!

Well-balanced life

My idea of well-being is having a balanced life through prioritizing. I have to regularly sit down with pen and paper, and then decide and write down what are the most important things to focus on at this particular time of my life. How can I please God in all of my actions? What am I longing for? How do I want to feel? What will bring me joy? I have to answer all of these questions and more to make a plan. After setting the priorities, I need to read them often to remind myself of what they are. My focus gets derailed sometimes, and since I am not a robot, I let myself have fun, and do what makes me feel alive and vibrant. Then I have more energy to do the "big" things in life, but do them with the attitude of a person who is still having fun.

Have I been working too hard lately and neglecting my family and health? Do I need to shift my attention to managing finances? Have I slowed down in my spiritual and mental growth? Has it been weeks since I read a good book or listened to an audio book? Be it family, work, spiritual life, or time with friends, when I pay too much attention to just one or two aspects, the rest gets out of balance. Then I realize that I need to come up with and implement a new, efficient game plane.

Occasionally, simple acts of self-care, relaxing and reading are the best things I can do to balance my newly rediscovered busy life. Traveling, health and fitness, as well as having fun with friends and family are truly rejuvenating and need to be taken seriously and scheduled accordingly. It is crucial for the overachiever's survival! Then I can think about how I can live my life to the fullest, thinking how to make it the most meaningful and exciting.

In the past few years I consciously submerged myself into the pain of anxiety symptoms to be able to help those who suffer and think there's no way out. Over time, this pain ceased to scare me as much as it did at first. Usually I just looked at it as an annoyance, waiting for it to pass. From time to time I went to the doctor for a check-up just to see that everything is okay, and it was. It's interesting because I wanted to become a doctor but never got the necessary education in this field. I really like all health related topics and studies. Attempting to help those who suffer from panic attacks is probably as close as I'll ever get to being a health practitioner. Even though I cannot give health advice, I can help through example with my story. I remember watching Oprah and her mentioning how she wanted to be a teacher, and she did, to millions of people on a global scale. Many may disagree with her opinions, but can't deny that she is passionate about helping people and that her intentions are based on love and compassion.

The Biggest Lesson From Writing This Book

The only time that all these symptoms were sure to return with a vengeance was during the writing of this book. So many people, including my doctors, encouraged me to share my path to healing with others. I was willing and excited to do it, but there was a big problem. Every time I worked on editing, eager to share my experiences with those who suffer, the pain of anxiety returned. It felt as bad as in the beginning. As soon as I put it on hold, I resumed a normal state. And so it became a vicious cycle for years. I wanted to share my story to help others, but the pain came back within days of my resuming writing. It soon became too intense and heavy to bear. I would have to stop for months to compose myself before venturing into painful memories again. It took numerous attempts to continue. At times I retreated in defeat when the pain became too intense. I had to put my notes aside, to lay dormant for months at a time. I then tried to write in short increments, watched a lot of comedy and took long breaks, slowly inching forward. It helped tremendously that on this journey I encountered numerous people who became encouragers. Again and again, people shared their stories of suffering. I was reminded that my story may help someone who is as miserable and lost as I was. This is what kept me going.

With prayer and taking breaks, I felt peace come over me as a super soft cuddly blanket, enveloping and shielding me from worry. It was a reminder of the Bible story of Jesus, when He calmed the storm on the Sea of Galilee, saying, "Peace! Be still." The Lord had calmed this particular storm in my life to encourage and show me His love, but not right away.

After long breaks, when I felt great again and thought about going back to writing, excitement overtook me. But then dwelling in past pain, as this sort of writing required, created a stirring of anxiety.

Along the way I was reminded over and over again of the consequences of dwelling in the past. Looking back at the past often brings painful experiences that trigger unwelcome emotions. Furthermore, we sometimes experience events that brought about those emotions in the first place over and over again. Was I to learn that looking back and reliving the past pain is harmful? Am I supposed to learn from events as they occur, grieve for an allotted time (depending on the event) and move on to God-given destiny? Some trials we face are so painful, we don't know how we can survive them, but God can miraculously heal our hearts and give meaning to our lives.

In the book of Genesis there is a story of Lot's family fleeing to Sodom and Gomorrah, two cities that were destined to destruction. As they were running away, they were told not to look back, only ahead. Temptation prevailed and Lot's wife turned to glance at the scene they were fleeing. Was she longing for a place that was so familiar, her friends and family, or was she curious about what was happening to the people who were doomed to their destruction? I will never know, but as she glanced back, she was immediately turned into a pillar of salt. It was a harsh punishment for such disobedience. She was initially spared from destruction and on her way to safety. She just wanted to look! Maybe this story was told to remind all of us that looking back may cost us dearly and we should not be too eager to do it. The past should stay in the past and only God knows our future. The only certainty we truly have is in the present moment, where we can make decisions and try to live to the fullest. Even if a person is sure about life after death, they are still frightened with the news of terminal disease diagnosis. It is also natural to grieve the passing of a loved one. In such heartbreaks, only God can heal an aching heart and comfort a throbbing soul.

Getting over painful memories is very difficult as well. Not releasing past mistakes, guilt or hurts causes constantly recurring pain. We must not relive the past and dwell in misery. The Lord forgave and forgot, so we have to follow this example of our Creator. Moving on takes courage. Sometimes we need encouragement to do so, maybe even from a psychologist. We cannot be ashamed to admit our weaknesses and need for help when we are stuck in emotional turmoil. When it is over, we will be able to look at our present in gratitude and joy, seeing our past as full of learning experiences. We do better to think of the good in our current lives as well as miraculous events from the past, which are the only worthy memories. As an outcome, our future becomes full of opportunities and possibilities, and brighter as we follow God's will.

I can choose to look at my past as full of misery and regret, pain and suffering, or full of lessons that God allowed for my growth. Putting a magnifying glass on past mistakes does not benefit me. We are placed here on earth to fulfill our divine destiny—let us focus on that. What can I do *now* to get closer to this ultimate goal is the real question at hand.

I am learning to live my life in gratitude. I try to do and say what I think will be pleasing to my Creator, to live life passionately by fulfilling my purpose in life, using God-given gifts and talents, counting my blessings daily. That is the only way I know to have truly **joyful** living.

Stress-Relief First-Aid Kit

- Prayer and meditation, peaceful solitude
- Deep breathing
- Make sure I have a posture of a warrior, not a worrier
- Smile and laugh
- Express my gratitude to God
- Mental check for triggers
- Return to God-focused life
- Exercise (walking, stretches, Pilates, cardio, dancing)
- Acupuncture
- Add supplements if needed
- Adjust diet, consume more alkaline foods, cut out caffeine, alcohol, refined carbohydrates, chocolate
- Expectation adjustment, flexibility and compromise
- Remove or limit contact with toxic people
- Nourish deep, meaningful, mutually supportive friendships
- Express rather than suppress feelings
- Nurture body and soul
- Spend time in nature, appreciating God's creation
- Make time for healthy distractions, activities or hobbies; reading, gardening, working on a puzzle, at least for a short while

Nowadays, on the rare occasion a cloud of anxiety hovering over me, I just ride through it. Thank God!

Scripture Verses

There are numerous passages in the Bible full of encouragement and promise:

"When anxiety was great within me, your consolations brought me joy." (Psalm 94:19)

"Anxiety in a man's heart weighs him down, but a good word makes him glad." (Proverbs 12:25, ESV)

"Cast your cares on the LORD and he will sustain you; he will never let the righteous be shaken." (Psalm 55:22)

"Cast all your anxiety on him because He cares for you." (1 Peter 5:7)

"Do not grieve, for the joy of the Lord is your strength." (Nehemiah 8:10)

"I lift up my eyes to the hills. From where does my help come? My help comes from the Lord, who made heaven and earth." (Psalm 121:1-2, ESV)

"O Lord my God, I cried out to You, and You healed me" (Psalm 30:2, NKJV)

"And ye shall serve the Lord your God, and he shall bless thy bread, and thy water; and I will take sickness away from the midst of thee." (Exodus 23:25)

"Praise the Lord, O my soul, and forget not all His benefits, Who forgives all your sins and heals all your diseases, Who redeems your life from the pit and crowns you with love and compassion." (Psalm 103:2-4)

"So don't worry about tomorrow, for tomorrow will bring its own worries. Today's trouble is enough for today." (Matthew 6:34, NLT)

"...do not be anxious about anything, but in everything by prayer and supplication with thanksgiving let your requests be made known to God. And the peace of God, which surpasses

all understanding, will guard your hearts and your minds in Christ Jesus." (Philippians 4:6-7, ESV)

"For I know the plans I have for you, declares The Lord, plans to prosper you, not to harm you; plans to give you hope and a future." (Jeremiah 29:11)

"You have made known to me the paths of life; you will fill me with joy in your presence." (Acts 2:28)

"Cast all your anxiety on him because he cares for you."(1 Peter 5:7)

"The Lord is my light and my salvation- whom shall I fear? The Lord is the stronghold of my life- of whom shall I be afraid?" (Psalm 27:1)

"So do not fear, for I am with you; do not be dismayed, for I am you God. I will strengthen you and help you; I will uphold you with my righteous hand." (Isaiah 41:10)

"The Lord is my strength and my shield; my heart trusts in him, and I am helped. My heart leaps for joy and I will give thanks to him in song." (Psalm 28:7)

Acknowledgments

It is with deepest gratitude that I dedicate this book to Kim and George. You never doubted my complete healing and gave love and support that comforted me every day. I will forever appreciate your love, kindness, encouragement and patience that sustained me on this journey. Having you by my side was and is the greatest blessing. I love you both with all my heart.

I am tremendously blessed to have friends and family who prayed for me, offered support and encouragement:

To Mom. Thank you for all the lessons you taught me. I love you much.

To Alexandr. Brother, you helped me, you put up with me, you led me to the Lord. Thank you.

To Bill Vlachos- in-depth conversations and laughter we shared were very therapeutic, encouraging and uplifting.

To Narmina Rasulova, Renata Chabot, Inna Yalch, Larisa Morgan, Zhanna Khurshudyan, Nancy Thompson, Jan Taylor, Kathy Manokian, Risa Parness Weddle, Roni Pearlman, Ila Lee, Kay Sumner, Gloria Stoop, Kathleen Brooks, and Carrie Aukerman.

To Carla Riehl, Stefanie Boyer, Cary Cary, Meridith Cary, Marina Cary, Paige Weslaski, Yvonne Sandbloom and most of all Joanna Mastopietro- my editorial team.

To Hans Stoop and Chuck Vaught for technical support.

To all doctors, psychologists and health care providers who assisted my speedy recovery. A special thank you to Dr. Susan Taylor- you offered guidance, support and expressed faith in my complete healing from the very beginning. You were the first person who encouraged me to write this book.

To all my dear friends who prayed for this book to become a reality.

To all my "Divine Appointments" along the way: to courageous men and women who opened up about their emotional and mental challenges. It is for you that I wrote this book.

Now I can confidently say: It has been a blessed journey.

Resources

On my journey to healing I perused numerous books and tapes. Unfortunately in the beginning I was so distraught I didn't keep track of what I have read or listened to thus I can't provide complete bibliography nor acknowledge by name every author whose work helped me to get where I am now. I would like to express deep gratitude to everyone who in his or her writing shone light on dark topic of mental illness and provided recommendations on getting out of tremendous pain it causes.

Fear and Other Uninvited Guests: Tackling the Anxiety, Fear and Shame that Keep Us from Optimal Living and Loving (CD set), by Harriet Lerner, Ph.D.

Feel the Fear and Do It Anyway: Dynamic Techniques for Turning Fear, Indecision, and Anger into Power, Action and Love (CD set), by Susan Jeffers, Ph.D.

Think and Grow Rich for Women (CD set), by Sharon Lechter

Coping With Anxiety: 10 Simple Ways to Relieve Anxiety, Fear and Worry, by Edmund Bourne, Ph.D. and Lorna Garano

From Panic to Power: Proven Techniques to Calm Your Anxieties, Conquer Your Fears, and Put You in Control of Your Life, by Lucinda Bassett

The Anxiety Cure: You Can Find Emotional Tranquillity and Wholeness, by Dr. Archibald D. Hart

One Perfect Word by Debbie Macomber

The 10 Best-Ever Anxiety Management Techniques: Understanding How Your Brain Makes You Anxious & What Can You Do to Change it, by Margaret Wehrenberg

Bottom Line's Ultimate Healing, World's Greatest Treasury of Health Secrets

Uncommon Cures for Everyday Ailments

One Small Step Can Change Your Life: The Kaizen Way, by Robert Maurer, Ph.D.

The Great Physician's Rx For Health And Wellness, by Jordan Rubin

Purpose Driven Life, by Rick Warren

Overcoming Panic Attacks, by Ray Comfort

Our Daily Bread, by RBC Ministries

First For Women, Magazine, Bauer Publishing Co.

Psychologytoday.com

Mercola.com

National Center for PTSD at *www.ncptsd.org*

Accupuncture.com

WebMD.com

Made in the USA
San Bernardino, CA
11 March 2017